TITLES IN THE POPULAR LECTURES IN MATHEMATICS SERIES

POPULAR LECTURES IN MATHEMATICS

Editors: I. N. SNEDDON *and* M. STARK

VOLUME 15

Successive Approximation

Successive Approximation

BY

N. Ya. VILENKIN

TRANSLATED AND ADAPTED FROM THE RUSSIAN BY

MICHAEL B. P. SLATER AND JOAN W. TELLER

SURVEY OF
RECENT EAST EUROPEAN MATHEMATICAL LITERATURE

A project conducted by
ALFRED L. PUTNAM and IZAAK WIRSZUP
Department of Mathematics,
The University of Chicago, under a
grant from the National Science Foundation

A Pergamon Press Book

THE MACMILLAN COMPANY
NEW YORK
1964

THE MACMILLAN COMPANY
60 Fifth Avenue, New York 11, N.Y.

This book is distributed by
THE MACMILLAN COMPANY
pursuant to a special arrangement with
PERGAMON PRESS LIMITED
Oxford, England

This book is an edited translation of
Metod posledovatel'nykh priblizhenii,
Moscow, 1961.

Library of Congress Catalog Card No. 64–14148

Set in 10 on 11 pt. Times N.R. and printed in Great Britain
at the PITMAN PRESS, BATH

CONTENTS

CONTENTS

PREFACE

THE primary aim of this booklet is to present a number of methods for the approximate solution of equations. Their practical value is indisputable, yet they are little studied in high school or college. It will often happen, therefore, that someone who may even have majored in mathematics will find it difficult to solve the simplest of transcendental equations. Not only engineers, but other specialists need to solve equations, and familiarity with methods of approximate solution of equations is useful for the high school and college student.

Since most of the methods for the approximate solution of equations are connected with the concept of the derivative, we have found it necessary to introduce this concept. We have based our treatment on an appeal to geometry, however. The reader therefore needs no more background than is provided by high school mathematics.

In compiling this book the author made use of a lecture he gave to ninth- and tenth-grade students in the school mathematics circle at Moscow State University.

The content of this lecture was adopted by S. I. Shvartsburd, a Moscow high school teacher, for work outside class hours with his ninth-grade pupils. The author thanks him for his solutions to some of the problems used for this book.

The author expresses his deep gratitude to V. G. Boltyanskii, whose suggestions improved the first version of the manuscript.

N. Ya. Vilenkin

1

INTRODUCTION

THE school mathematics program devotes a great deal of time to solving equations and systems of equations. One first meets equations of the first degree, and systems of such equations. Then quadratic, biquadratic, and irrational equations appear. Finally, one learns about exponential, logarithmic, and trigonometric equations.

This concentration on equations is deliberate. It is explained by the important role played by equations in applied mathematics. Whatever area of application we may think of, we will almost always find that the final answer to some problem is to be obtained by solving an equation or a system of equations.

As an example, we often need equations for the solution of school physics problems. Consider this problem: *A stone is dropped in a well. Find the depth of the well given that you hear the sound of the stone's hitting bottom after T sec.*

If we denote the depth of the well by x, we have the following equation for determining it:

$$\sqrt{\left(\frac{2x}{g}\right)} + \frac{x}{v} = T,$$

where v is the speed of propagation of sound in air, the first term is the time the stone takes to the bottom, and the second is the time the sound takes to reach us. This is an *irrational* equation. If we write $\sqrt{x} = y$ we can rewrite the equation in the form

$$\frac{y^2}{v} + \sqrt{\left(\frac{2}{g}\right)} y - T = 0,$$

which can be solved with the quadratic formula.

Equations may also be used in solving geometric problems. Suppose we wish to divide a segment AB in the golden ratio, that is, to find a point C between A and B such that $AB/AC = AC/CB$. This leads to the quadratic equation

$$x^2 + lx - l^2 = 0,$$

where l is the length of AB and x of AC.

1

We are led to a more complex equation when we investigate the problem of trisecting an angle α. The equation is

$$4x^3 - 3x - \cos \alpha = 0,$$

where $x = \cos \frac{1}{3}\alpha$. In algebra courses it is sometimes shown that a formula for the solution of cubic equations does exist (see formula (3) below).

We often come across problems in physics that lead to more complicated equations, however—equations for which no formulas for the solutions are given either in school or in college. Consider a steel beam clamped firmly at each end. If we strike it, it will start oscillating transversely. It is shown in mathematical physics that if we are to find the frequency of these oscillations, we must first solve the equation

$$e^x + e^{-x} = \frac{2}{\cos x}, \tag{1}$$

where $e = 2.71828.\ \ldots$

No methods are taught in school for solving such an equation. This is not explainable, as one might suppose, by the limited time available for mathematics in school. Formulas for the solution of equations such as (1), in the high school sense of the word, simply *do not exist*. Let us put our assertion more precisely.

We say that a formula exists for the solution of an equation if we may express its roots in terms of the constants appearing in the equation by means of arithmetic operations, the exponential, logarithmic, trigonometric, and inverse trigonometric functions. In this sense the quadratic equation $x^2 - 2px + q$ has the following formula for its solution:

$$x = p + \sqrt{(p^2 - q)}. \tag{2}$$

A formula exists for the solution of the general cubic equation $a_0 x^3 + a_1 x^2 + a_2 x + a_3 = 0$ (with $a_0 \neq 0$). On substituting

$$x = \frac{y}{(a_0)^{\frac{1}{3}}} - \frac{a_1}{3a_0},$$

we may reduce the general cubic to the form

$$y^3 + 3py - 2q = 0,$$

which has the real root

$$y = [q + \sqrt{(q^2 - p^3)}]^{\frac{1}{3}} + [q - \sqrt{(q^2 + p^3)}]^{\frac{1}{3}}. \tag{3}$$

The practical application of formula (3) is sometimes difficult, however, and may require the use of complex numbers.

There is a formula for the solution of the general quartic (or biquadratic) equation, but it is so complicated that we will not produce it.

Equations of the fifth and higher degrees are not so simple. In 1826 the Norwegian mathematician Abel proved that no formula exists for the solution of the general algebraic equation

$$a_0 x^n + a_1 x^{n-1} + \ldots + a_n = 0$$

of degree n greater than 4. Only in special cases do formulas exist for solving algebraic equations of high degree.

If mathematicians limited themselves to the study of equations with exact solutions given by a formula, we might hear such a conversation between a mathematician and an engineer:

ENGINEER: I have been designing a piece of equipment, and this equation came up (he shows the mathematician the equation). I must solve this equation quickly. The design has to be ready in a month.

MATHEMATICIAN: I would be glad to help you, but there is no formula for the solution of this sort of equation.

ENGINEER: Well, could you work out a formula for me?

MATHEMATICIAN: I wouldn't even try. It was proved long ago that no formulas exist for the solution of this kind of equation.

After such a conversation the engineer's opinion of the powers of mathematics would fall sharply. Fortunately, such conversations do not occur. The engineer usually does not need a formula to solve an equation. He needs only a root of the equation accurate to within a certain error, and whether a formula or some other method is used is a minor matter, for he will usually only need the formula to calculate the root to the necessary accuracy.

Imagine that a formula is known for the solution of a certain equation, and that on applying it the engineer finds a root $x = 3 + \sqrt{13}$. It is clear that this solution cannot be used as it stands (after all, you could hardly ask a machinist to turn a shaft of diameter $3 + \sqrt{13}$ in.). For practical purposes you have to express $\sqrt{13}$ as a decimal fraction, taking a number of decimal places appropriate to the tolerance to which you are working.

Thus the engineer will be satisfied if the mathematician gives him *any* method of calculating roots of an equation to the required accuracy. Many methods have been developed in mathematics for the approximate solution of equations. The purpose of this book is to describe some of them.

3

2

SUCCESSIVE APPROXIMATIONS

MOST of the methods for the approximate solution of equations are based on the idea of *successive approximations*. This idea is applied not only to the solution of equations, but also to the solution of a wide variety of practical problems.

A gunner would use a process of successive approximation. If he wants to hit a target, he starts by taking aim and firing. If he misses and can see where his shell exploded, he can make appropriate corrections in his aim and fire again. After a number of such "approximations," the aim will be good enough to hit the target.

Sometimes successive approximations are required even to determine the point of aim. Suppose you have an antiaircraft gun at the point O and you are firing at a flying airplane (Fig. 1). If you aim

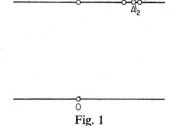

Fig. 1

at the point A_0, which is where the airplane is, you will miss, since the plane will have moved to the point A_1 during the time the shell is in the air. It is easy to calculate the position of the point A_1, knowing the speed of your shell and the plane. If instead of aiming at A_0 you aim at A_1 in the first place, you may still miss. You are now aiming at an angle, so that the shell will take longer to reach A_1 than it would to reach A_0. In the extra time the plane will have reached A_2. The distance from A_1 to A_2 will be much less than the distance from A_0 to A_1, however. To make the shot still closer, you

4

could aim at A_2, or go on to calculate that by the time your shell reaches A_2 the plane will be at A_3, and aim at A_3 instead. After a number of such approximations you will be able to aim the shell so that it comes close enough to hit the plane (say, within 10 ft).

The method of successive approximations is used for the solution of many other problems as well.

Suppose you have to transport sand from a number of sand quarries $A_1, \ldots, A_n$ to a number of building sites $B_1, \ldots, B_m$. Suppose the quarry A_j produces a_j tons of sand a day and the building site B_k requires b_k tons of sand a day. Suppose, finally, that the cost of transporting 1 ton of sand from quarry A_j to site B_k is c_{jk}. (This quantity will depend on the distance between A_j and B_k, the state of the road between them, and other factors.)

To determine our plan of delivery we draw up Table 1. Here

TABLE 1

	B_1	B_2	. . .	B_m
A_1	x_{11}	x_{12}	. . .	x_{1m}
A_2	x_{21}	x_{22}	. . .	x_{2m}
. . .	. . .	. . .	. . .	. . .
A_n	x_{n1}	x_{n2}	. . .	x_{nm}

x_{jk} denotes the quantity of sand to be taken from A_j to B_k each day. It is clear that the x_{jk} have to satisfy the following relationship:

$$x_{j1} + x_{j2} + \ldots + x_{jm} \leqslant a_j$$

since you cannot take more than a_j tons of sand from A_j in a day, and

$$x_{1k} + x_{2k} + \ldots + x_{nk} = b_k$$

since b_k tons of sand are required at B_k each day.

According to Table 1, the total daily cost of transporting sand is given by

$$\begin{aligned}
C = \; & c_{11}x_{11} + c_{12}x_{12} + \ldots + c_{1n}x_{1n} \\
& + c_{21}x_{21} + c_{22}x_{22} + \ldots + c_{2n}x_{2n} \\
& \cdot \cdot \cdot \cdot \cdot \cdot \cdot \cdot \cdot \cdot \cdot \cdot \cdot \cdot \\
& + c_{m1}x_{m1} + c_{m2}x_{m2} + \ldots + c_{mn}x_{mn}.
\end{aligned} \quad (4)$$

We must adopt a plan that makes C minimal. As a first attempt, we might assign to the quarry A_1 the nearest building site to it, say, B_j. If A_1 produces more sand than B_j requires, we assign another site B_k to A_1, choosing the next closest one. After a number of such steps we will exhaust the daily productivity of A_1. If, on the other hand, B_j requires more sand than A_1 produces, we assign another quarry A_i to B_j, choosing the next closest one to B_j. Continuing in this sort of way we shall finally have assigned quarries to every site, and sites to every quarry.

The plan we have devised in this way may not be the best, however, as we are finally left with only a few sites, and they may be very far from the remaining quarries. Some of the sites that we assigned to the first quarries will have to be reassigned to other quarries.

Methods of changing plans in order to reduce the total cost are dealt with in the branch of mathematics called *linear programming*. A booklet on the subject has been published in this series.†

After a number of successive changes in plan, made in accordance with the schemes devised in linear programming, we will reach a plan for which the sum C is a minimum, or differs little from it.

In general, in devising a plan, a timetable, or the like, we start with a crude approximation, and then improve it step by step until the required result is achieved.

The machining of a part in a metal shop or a factory can be regarded as a sequence of successively better approximations to the required shape. First one takes a crude approximation—a casting or some other stock. This stock is machined to a form approximating that of the required part. It is then taken to another machine which works to greater accuracy. After a number of steps (successive approximations), the required part emerges.

† Barsov, *What is Linear Programming?*, Boston: D. C. Heath, 1963, or see A. Charnes, *Lectures on the Mathematical Theory of Linear Programming* (Part II of W. W. Cooper, *An Introduction to Linear Programming*, New York, Wiley, 1953).

3

ACHILLES AND THE TORTOISE

THE first discussion of successive approximations is found in the work of Zeno of Elea, who lived around 500 B.C. This philosopher tried to prove that there is no such thing as motion. Zeno's argument ran as follows: Achilles, the swiftest of the Greeks, will never catch up in a race with a tortoise. Suppose that Achilles starts out 1000 paces behind the tortoise, and that he runs at a rate of 10 paces a second, while the tortoise crawls 1 pace a second. After 100 sec Achilles will have covered the 1000 paces separating him from the tortoise. But during this period the tortoise will have crawled 100 paces further. After another 10 sec Achilles will have covered these 100 paces, but the tortoise will still be 10 paces ahead. To cover these 10 paces, Achilles needs only 1 sec, but meanwhile the tortoise has advanced 1 pace more. Thus the tortoise will always be ahead of Achilles. But this is ridiculous. The only conclusion is that motion is an illusion.

Of course, Zeno's argument is a brilliant paradox, but it does not prove that motion cannot exist. We shall not be concerned with the philosophical points raised by the paradox, but regard it, rather, as a method of successive approximation to the place and time where Achilles catches up with the tortoise. Any schoolboy can calculate this easily: if x is the required time, we form the equation

$$1000 = 10x - x \tag{5}$$

and deduce

$$x = \frac{1000}{9} \text{ sec} = 111\tfrac{1}{9} \text{ sec.}$$

To translate Zeno's approximating argument into mathematical terms we proceed as follows: suppose we have found an approximate solution x_n of our problem. By the conditions of the problem the tortoise will have crawled x_n paces in this time. Achilles takes $x_n/10$ sec to run x_n paces. Furthermore he takes 100 sec to run the

2

first 1000 paces that originally separated him from the tortoise. So to arrive at the place where the tortoise was after x_n sec, Achilles needs x_{n+1} sec, where

$$x_{n+1} = 100 + \frac{x_n}{10}. \qquad (6)$$

Setting $x_0 = 0$, we obtain the successive numbers $x_1 = 100$, $x_2 = 110$, $x_3 = 111$, $x_4 = 111.1, \ldots$, which are the same numbers that turned up in Zeno's argument. As n increases the numbers x_n approach closer and closer to the exact solution $x = 111\frac{1}{9}$ sec of equation (5).

Let us note that the formula (6) is closely connected with equation (5), for we may rewrite the equation in the form

$$x = 100 + \frac{x}{10}. \qquad (7)$$

On substituting the value $x_0 = 0$ for x in the right side of (7) we find $x_1 = 100$; on substituting this value for x in the right side we find $x_2 = 110$, and so on.

In the example given here the numbers $x_1, x_2, \ldots, x_n, \ldots$, approached the solution $111\frac{1}{9}$ of equation (5). Had Achilles been racing an antelope instead of a tortoise, this process of successive approximation would have failed. Suppose the antelope runs at a rate of 20 paces a second. Then our equation would be

$$1000 = 10x - 20x, \qquad (8)$$

and the approximating formula would be

$$x_{n+1} = 100 + 2x_n. \qquad (9)$$

If in this case we started by setting $x_0 = 0$, we would find $x_1 = 100$, $x_2 = 200$, $x_3 = 300, \ldots$

Thus the sequence $x_1, x_2, \ldots, x_n, \ldots$, would not approach the solution $x = -100$ of equation (8). This is not surprising, since after 100 sec the antelope will be 2000 paces ahead of Achilles, and thereafter the distance between them will continue to increase. It is natural, therefore, that the method of successive approximation will not yield a solution here.

8

4

DIVISION ON
DIGITAL COMPUTERS

THE reader may wonder why we had to solve equation (5) by successive approximation instead of simply solving it directly. But, of course, we were interested not so much in equation (5) as in the method of successive approximation, which we intend to apply later to more complex equations.

It should be pointed out, however, that the solution by successive approximation of equations such as (5) is carried out on certain high-speed digital computers that cannot perform division in any other way. Such a digital computer can carry out the three fundamental arithmetical operations—addition, subtraction, and multiplication. It can also divide by numbers of the form 2^n. How are such machines to divide by any number?

The division of the number b by the number a is the process of finding the solution of the equation $ax = b$. Since the machine can multiply and divide by powers of 2, we may suppose that $\frac{1}{2} \leqslant a \leqslant 1$. If this is not so, we can either divide or multiply both sides of the equation $ax = b$ by an appropriate power of 2. We now rewrite the equation in the form

$$x = (1 - a)x + b. \tag{10}$$

As our first approximation for x we take $x_1 = b$. Suppose our error is α_1 (positive or negative), that is, suppose $x_1 + \alpha_1 = b/a$. Then from (10) we obtain

$$x_1 + \alpha_1 = (1 - a)(x_1 + \alpha_1) + b$$
$$= (1 - a)x_1 + b + (1 - a)\alpha_1. \tag{11}$$

Since a lies between $\frac{1}{2}$ and 1, we have

$$0 \leqslant 1 - a \leqslant \tfrac{1}{2}.$$

Because of this, the summand $(1 - a)\alpha_1$ on the right side is at most half as large as α_1. So we discard it and obtain

$$x_1 + \alpha_1 \approx (1 - a)x_1 + b.$$

The number $x_2 = (1 - a)x_1 + b$ is our next approximation to x.

Let us denote by α_2 the error in our approximation x_2, that is, we suppose $x_2 + \alpha_2 = b/a$. We know that α_2 is at most half as big as α_1. From equation (10) we now obtain

$$x_2 + \alpha_2 = (1 - a)x_2 + b + (1 - a)\alpha_2.$$

Rejecting the summand $(1 - a)\alpha_2$ we obtain the approximation

$$x_2 + \alpha_2 \approx (1 - a)x_2 + b.$$

We may therefore take the next approximation to be

$$x_3 = (1 - a)x_2 + b.$$

Arguing in the same way, we find that the next approximation is

$$x_4 = (1 - a)x_3 + b,$$

and so on. Each of the numbers $x_1, x_2, \ldots, x_n, \ldots$, is obtained successively from the formula

$$x_{n+1} = (1 - a)x_n + b, \tag{12}$$

and our argument shows that the error of each number is at most half the error of its predecessor. Thus the numbers approach indefinitely close to b/a. This formula needs only the operations of addition, multiplication, and subtraction, however, and therefore can be used by a digital computer.

As a matter of fact, the method we have described for division is based on the formula for the sum of an infinite geometric series. We may write the fraction b/a in the form

$$\frac{b}{a} = \frac{b}{1 - (1 - a)}.$$

But according to the formula,

$$\frac{b}{1 - (1 - a)} = b + b(1 - a) + b(1 - a)^2 + \ldots$$
$$+ b(1 - a)^{n-1} + \ldots \tag{13}$$

Let us denote by x_n the sum of the first n terms of this series:

$$x_n = b + b(1 - a) + \ldots + b(1 - a)^{n-1}.$$

10

It is clear that

$$x_{n+1} = b + b(1 - a) + \ldots + b(1 - a)^n$$
$$= b + (1 - a)[b + b(1 - a) + \ldots + b(1 - a)^{n-1}]$$
$$= b + (1 - a)x_n.$$

This formula coincides with (12). Also $x_1 = b$ coincides with our choice of a first approximation. Thus our approximation x_n for the value of b/a amounts to replacing an infinite sum (13) by the sum of its first n terms. As n increases, this finite sum approaches indefinitely close to the infinite sum. We have already seen that the difference between x_{n+1} and b/a is at most half the difference between x_n and b/a, and therefore the error of x_{n+1} is at most $1/2^n[(b/a) - b]$, which tends to zero as n increases indefinitely.

5

EXTRACTING SQUARE ROOTS BY SUCCESSIVE APPROXIMATION

WE now show how we can use the method of successive approximation to extract square roots. A method for doing this is taught in school, and it allows us to determine the successive decimal places of the root, one by one. This method can be regarded as one method of successive approximation to the solution. It is rather complicated, however, and pupils are apt to apply it mechanically, without understanding the underlying idea. We shall describe a different method, which was used in Babylon hundreds of years B.C. It was also used by the mathematician Hero, of Alexandria. Later, this method fell into disuse, but it is now used for extracting square roots on certain digital computers. Suppose we are to take the square root of 28. We first choose an approximate value for the root, say $x_1 = 5$. We denote the error by α_1, so that $\sqrt{28} = 5 + \alpha_1$. To find the value of α_1, we square both sides of this equation. We find that

$$28 = 25 + 10\alpha_1 + \alpha_1^2,$$

that is,

$$\alpha_1^2 + 10\alpha_1 - 3 = 0. \tag{14}$$

We have thus obtained a quadratic equation for α_1. If we try to solve this equation exactly, we obtain the roots $\alpha_1 = -5 \pm \sqrt{28}$. Thus to determine α_1 exactly, we must first find $\sqrt{28}$. We seem to be in a vicious circle: to find $\sqrt{28}$ we need α_1, and to find α_1 we need $\sqrt{28}$.

The following consideration allows us to escape: the error α_1 of the approximate solution $x_1 = 5$ is not large (it is surely less than 1). So α_1^2 will be still smaller. Let us therefore find an approximate value for α_1 by disregarding the small term α_1^2 in equation (14). We obtain an approximate equation for α_1: $10\alpha_1 - 3 \approx 0$, giving us the approximate value $\alpha_1 \approx 0.3$.

We have thus found an approximate value of the correction term α_1. Since $\sqrt{28} = 5 + \alpha_1$, our second approximation x_2 for $\sqrt{28}$ will be

$$x_2 = 5 + 0.3 = 5.3.$$

To find an even more accurate approximation to $\sqrt{28}$ we repeat the process. We denote the error in the solution $x_2 = 5.3$ by α_2. That is, $\sqrt{28} = x_2 + \alpha_2$. We square both sides of this equation and reject the small term α_2^2. We find that $28 \approx x_2^2 + 2x_2\alpha_2$, and therefore that

$$\alpha_2 \simeq \frac{28 - x_2^2}{2x_2}.$$

This means that our third approximation to $\sqrt{28}$ is given by the formula

$$x_3 = x_2 + \frac{28 - x_2^2}{2x_2} = \frac{28 + x_2^2}{2x_2}.$$

Since $x_2 = 5.3$, we find that $x_3 = 5.2915.\,\ldots\,$ In the same way, starting from the approximate value $x_3 = 5.2915$, we find a further approximation x_4 to the solution, given by

$$x_4 = \frac{28 + x_3^2}{2x_3} = 5.2915 \ldots$$

In general, if we already have an approximate value x_n for $\sqrt{28}$, our next approximation will be

$$x_{n+1} = \frac{28 + x_n^2}{2x_n}. \tag{15}$$

Each successive step brings us closer to the exact value. We may cut the sequence short whenever the difference between x_{n+1} and x_n becomes less than the margin of error we can tolerate. If we are computing $\sqrt{28}$ to an accuracy of 0.0001, for example, it is enough to calculate four approximations and to take $\sqrt{28} = 5.2915$. For both x_3 and x_4 are of the form 5.2915. . . .

We may likewise extract the square root of any positive number. Thus to find $\sqrt{a}$ we choose a first approximation x_1 and then compute the successive approximations according to the formula

$$x_{n+1} = \frac{a + x_n^2}{2x_n}. \tag{16}$$

Formula (16) may be derived by a somewhat different argument from the one we used in calculating $\sqrt{28}$. Suppose we have already found the nth approximation x_n to $\sqrt{a}$. Since $\sqrt{a} = \sqrt{[x_n(a/x_n)]}$, $\sqrt{a}$ is the geometric mean of x_n and a/x_n. As an approximation to this *geometric mean* we take the *arithmetic mean* of the numbers by setting

$$x_{n+1} = \frac{1}{2}\left(x_n + \frac{a}{x_n}\right) = \frac{x_n^2 + a}{2x_n}.$$

This is precisely formula (16).

Thus the method described earlier is equivalent to approximating at each stage the geometric mean of the numbers x_n and a/x_n by their arithmetic mean.

We shall now determine whether this method of successively approximating a square root always works, that is, whether things will always turn out as they did when Achilles raced the tortoise and never as when he raced the antelope. In the first case mathematicians say that the sequence of approximations *converges*, and in the second that it *diverges*. We shall show that no complications arise in our process for extracting square roots—that the sequence of approximations always converges.

To do so we compare the errors $\alpha_n = \sqrt{a} - x_n$ and α_{n+1} $\sqrt{a} - x_{n+1}$ of two successive approximations. By formula (16) the error α_{n+1} can be written

$$\alpha_{n+1} = \sqrt{a} - x_{n+1} = \sqrt{a} - \frac{x_n^2 + a}{2x_n} = -\frac{x_n^2 - 2x_n\sqrt{a} + a}{2x_n}.$$

But

$$x_n^2 - 2x_n\sqrt{a} + a = (x_n - \sqrt{a})^2 = \alpha_n^2,$$

and therefore

$$\alpha_{n+1} = -\frac{\alpha_n^2}{2x_n}. \tag{17}$$

We are considering only positive approximations x_n to $\sqrt{a}$. We can therefore deduce from equation (17) that all the errors α_2, α_3, . . ., α_n, . . ., are negative. In other words, every approximation x_n, starting with x_2, is an approximation from above. This is true because the arithmetic mean of unequal numbers is always greater than their geometric mean. Of course, the first approximation may be either smaller or larger than the correct value.

Using formula (17) we may easily prove that the absolute values of the successive errors are at least halved at each step. We can write (17) as

$$\alpha_{n+1} = -\frac{\alpha_n}{2x_n}\alpha_n = \frac{x_n - \sqrt{a}}{2x_n}\alpha_n = \left(\frac{1}{2} - \frac{\sqrt{a}}{2x_n}\right)\alpha_n.$$

Thus

$$|\alpha_{n+1}| = \left|\frac{1}{2} - \frac{\sqrt{a}}{2x_n}\right||\alpha_n|. \tag{18}$$

But since $x_n > 0$

$$\frac{1}{2} - \frac{\sqrt{a}}{2x_n} < \frac{1}{2}.$$

On the other hand, we have shown above that for $n \geqslant 2$ we have $x_n > \sqrt{a}$, and therefore

$$\frac{1}{2} - \frac{\sqrt{a}}{2x_n} > 0.$$

From this we deduce the inequality

$$\left|\frac{1}{2} - \frac{\sqrt{a}}{2x_n}\right| < \frac{1}{2}. \tag{19}$$

Comparing (18) with (19) we see that

$$|\alpha_{n+1}| < \tfrac{1}{2}|\alpha_n|.$$

This proves our assertion. It follows that after the second approximation we have at least quartered our original error, after the third stage divided it by at least 8, and so on. It is clear that as n increases the absolute value of the error $\alpha_n = \sqrt{a} - x_n$ decreases steadily to zero. But this means that x_n tends to $\sqrt{a}$ as n increases.

Let us consider now the effect of our first choice x_1 on the sequence of approximations. We first note that our choice makes no difference in the end result, for we have already proved that whatever our initial (positive) approximation x_1, the successive errors α_2, α_3, . . ., α_n, . . ., of later approximations tend to zero. Thus if we are told the accuracy within which we have to calculate $\sqrt{a}$, we can always reach this degree of accuracy after a sufficient number of steps. Even if we make a bad first choice, we finally attain the correct value within the specified margin of error. After ten steps the absolute value of our error will have decreased by a factor of over 1000 ($2^{10} = 1024 \approx 1000$), and after forty steps by at least a thousand billion (10^{12}). Thus if we start with the guess of a million

(10^6) for $\sqrt{2}$, then $\alpha_1 \approx 10^6$, and therefore $|\alpha_{40}| < 10^{-6}$. In other words, our initial error was close to a million and our final error to a millionth.

Nevertheless, the choice of a first approximation does have an effect on the number of approximations we need to calculate to reach a certain accuracy. If we make a bad first choice, we shall have a long wait before x_n gets close to the true value. A good first choice speeds up the process considerably. We therefore often take the first approximation x_1 from a table of square roots and use the formula

$$x_2 = \frac{a + x_1^2}{2x_1} \tag{20}$$

merely to obtain a *better* approximation.

Such a procedure is especially valuable because the speed with which the approximations improve increases greatly when x_n is close to $\sqrt{a}$. In deducing the inequality

$$|\alpha_{n+1}| < \tfrac{1}{2}|\alpha_n|$$

we replaced a factor $|\tfrac{1}{2} - (\sqrt{a}/2x_n)|$ in (18) by $\tfrac{1}{2}$. But if x_n is close to $\sqrt{a}$, then the value $\tfrac{1}{2} - (\sqrt{a}/2x_n)$ is very small, and therefore

$$|\alpha_{n+1}| = \left| \frac{1}{2} - \frac{\sqrt{a}}{2} \right| |\alpha_n|$$

is considerably smaller than $\tfrac{1}{2}|\alpha_n|$.

Let us make this more precise. We consider together with the absolute error $|\alpha_n| = |\sqrt{a} - x_n|$ the *relative error* β_n of the approximating value x_n (the ratio of the absolute error $|\alpha_n|$ to the exact value of $\sqrt{a}$). This error is given by the formula

$$\beta_n = \frac{|\alpha_n|}{\sqrt{a}} = \left| 1 - \frac{x_n}{\sqrt{a}} \right|.$$

From (17) we find this formula for the value of β_{n+1}:

$$\beta_{n+1} = \frac{|\alpha_{n+1}|}{\sqrt{a}} = \frac{|\alpha_n|^2}{2x_n\sqrt{a}}.$$

Since $x_n > \sqrt{a}$, it follows that

$$\beta_{n+1} < \frac{|\alpha_n|^2}{2(\sqrt{a})^2} = \frac{1}{2}\beta_n^2.$$

16

Thus the relative errors β_n of the approximate values satisfy the inequality

$$\beta_{n+1} < \frac{\beta_n^2}{2}. \tag{21}$$

For instance, if the relative error of the approximation x_n is 0.01, then for x_{n+1} it will not be greater than 0.00005, and for x_{n+2} it will not be greater than 0.00000000013. We see that the accuracy of the approximations increases more and more rapidly. We can show that every successive approximation (once we are sufficiently close to $\sqrt{a}$) approximately doubles the number of correct decimal places.

EXAMPLE. Calculate $\sqrt{238}$ to an accuracy of 0.00001.

Using a four-place table, we find the value 15.43 for $\sqrt{238}$. Let us take this value for x_1 and find x_2 by the formula

$$x_2 = \frac{15.43^2 + 238}{30.86} = 15.42725 \ldots$$

What is the degree of accuracy of this estimate? Since the error in the value 15.43 is not greater than 0.01, we may safely take $\alpha_1 = 0.01$, and therefore

$$\beta_1 \approx \frac{0.01}{15.43} < 0.001.$$

But then

$$\beta_2 < \frac{0.001^2}{2} = 0.0000005.$$

This means that the absolute error of our approximation x_2 is not greater than $15.43(0.0000005) < 0.00001$. In other words, all five decimal places in the value 15.42725 for $\sqrt{238}$ are correct.

If we wanted to calculate the square root to *fourteen* decimal places, a third approximation would be enough. Such a degree of accuracy is never needed in practice, however.

Let us conclude this chapter by noting a special characteristic of our method of successive approximation. In the ordinary method of taking a square root, any mistake, at any stage, completely invalidates all subsequent calculations. This is not true of our method of successive approximation. Suppose we make a mistake, obtaining y_n where we should have obtained x_n. Then all our subsequent work may be regarded as the process of obtaining $\sqrt{a}$ from the initial value y_n. But we saw above that *whatever* our first choice we will always ultimately get as close as we like to $\sqrt{a}$. Thus the error we have committed will tend to zero, and its only effect will be to force us to calculate a number of extra approximations.

Because of this property, we may calculate our early approximations to a smaller number of decimal places, and use the required number only in the later ones. This saves us some unnecessary calculation.

6

EXTRACTING kTH ROOTS BY SUCCESSIVE APPROXIMATION

THE method described in the last section for extracting square roots can be applied to the extraction of kth roots for any positive integer k. We shall need the following formula:

$$(x + \alpha)^k = x^k + kx^{k-1}\alpha + \ldots, \qquad (22)$$

where the dots replace terms containing higher powers of α: α^2, α^3, and so on. This is part of Newton's binomial theorem, but we do not assume that the reader is acquainted with it.

Let us prove formula (22). It is well known from high school mathematics that

$$(x + \alpha)^2 = x^2 + 2x\alpha + \alpha^2,$$
$$(x + \alpha)^3 = x^3 + 3x^2\alpha + 3x\alpha^2 + \alpha^3.$$

We can rewrite these formulas in the following form:

$$(x + \alpha)^2 = x^2 + 2x\alpha + \ldots, \qquad (23)$$
$$(x + \alpha)^3 = x^3 + 3x^2\alpha + \ldots \qquad (24)$$

Thus we have proved formula (22) for $k = 2$ and $k = 3$. Let us now multiply both sides of (24) by $x + \alpha$. We find that

$$(x + \alpha)^4 = (x^3 + 3x^2\alpha + \ldots)(x + \alpha).$$

If we expand the right side, we obtain one summand x^4 containing no power of α, and two summands $3x^3\alpha$ and $x^3\alpha$ containing α to the first power. All the other summands will contain α to the second or a higher power. We may therefore write

$$(x + \alpha)^4 = x^4 + 3x^3\alpha + x^3\alpha + \ldots = x^4 + 4x^3\alpha + \ldots, \quad (25)$$

where, as in (22), the dots denote terms containing higher powers of α.

We have thus proved formula (22) for $k = 4$ as well as for $k = 2$

and $k = 3$. In the same way we may prove from formula (25) that

$$(x + \alpha)^5 = x^5 + 5x^4 + \ldots \qquad (26)$$

It is clear that the same process of proof establishes (22) for any positive integer k.

We now return to the problem of extracting kth roots. Suppose we already have some approximation x_1 to $\sqrt[k]{a}$. We denote, as usual, the error in this approximation by α_1, so that $x_1 + \alpha_1 = \sqrt[k]{a}$. Then $(x_1 + \alpha_1)^k = a$. But by formula (22) this equation can be written

$$x_1^k + kx_1^{k-1}\alpha_1 + \ldots = a,$$

where the dots again replace terms with powers of α_1 higher than the first.

If our approximation x_1 is close to $\sqrt[k]{a}$, then the error α_1 is small, and therefore we may neglect terms containing high powers of this error. We thus obtain an approximate equality

$$x_1^k + kx_1^{k-1}\alpha_1 \approx a.$$

From this equality it follows that

$$\alpha_1 \approx \frac{a - x_1^k}{kx_1^{k-1}},$$

and therefore we take as our second approximation to $\sqrt[k]{a}$

$$x_2 = x_1 + \frac{a - x_1^k}{kx_1^{k-1}} = \frac{a + (k - 1)x_1^k}{kx_1^{k-1}}.$$

In the same way, starting from x_2, we find our next approximation

$$x_3 = \frac{a + (k - 1)x_2^k}{kx_2^{k-1}}.$$

In general, if we have found an approximation x_n to $\sqrt[k]{a}$, then we take as our next approximation

$$x_{n+1} = \frac{a + (k - 1)x_n^k}{kx_n^{k-1}}. \qquad (27)$$

As in the case of square roots, it may be proved that this process will converge to $\sqrt[k]{a}$ whatever our choice of x_1 (so long as it is positive). In other words, for any positive number x_1 the sequence $x_1, x_2, \ldots, x_n, \ldots$, where for each n, x_{n+1} is calculated from x_n

by formula (27), will tend to $\sqrt[k]{a}$. To calculate $\sqrt[k]{a}$ to within a certain error, we continue the process of approximation until x_n and x_{n+1} coincide to the appropriate number of decimal places.

EXAMPLE. Calculate $\sqrt[3]{970}$ to within 0.001.

With $k = 3$ our approximating formula (27) takes the form

$$x_{n+1} = \frac{a + 2x_n^3}{3x_n^2}. \tag{28}$$

In our case $a = 970$. We choose $x_1 = 10$. It follows from (28) that

$$x_2 = \frac{970 + 2 \cdot 10^3}{3 \cdot 10^2} = \frac{2970}{300} = 9.900,$$

$$x_3 = \frac{970 + 2 \cdot 9.9^3}{3 \cdot 9.9^2} = \frac{2910.60}{294.03} = 9.899.$$

We see that x_2 and x_3 coincide to within the specified error. Thus

$$\sqrt[3]{970} = 9.899$$

to within 0.001.

7

THE DERIVATIVE OF A POLYNOMIAL

THE extraction of the kth root of a number a may be regarded as a process of solution of the equation

$$x^k - a = 0.$$

The problem is thus a special case of the following problem: given an algebraic equation, that is, an equation of the form

$$a_0 x^k + a_1 x^{k-1} + \ldots + a_k = 0$$

to find an approximate solution.

In the next section we describe Newton's method of approximately solving such equations, which is a direct generalization of the method we described for extracting kth roots. We shall start by introducing the concept of a *derivative*, one of the central concepts of higher mathematics. For the time being we define the derivative only for polynomials.

Let

$$f(x) = a_0 x^k + a_1 x^{k-1} + \ldots + a_k$$

be any polynomial function. We consider the polynomial $f(x + \alpha)$, that is, the expression

$$a_0(x + \alpha)^k + a_1(x + \alpha)^{k-1} + \ldots + a_k. \qquad (29)$$

If we remove the parentheses in (29), then some of the resulting terms will not contain α, some will have α appearing to the first power, some to the second, some to the third, and so on. We shall group the terms together to obtain an expression

$$f(x + \alpha) = f_0(x) + f_1(x)\alpha + f_2(x)\alpha^2 + \ldots + f_k(x)\alpha^k. \qquad (30)$$

Since the polynomial f is of degree k, the highest power of α that appears in (30) is precisely k. It is clear that $f_0(x)$, $f_1(x)$, . . ., $f_k(x)$ are all polynomials in x.

22

EXAMPLE. Suppose

$$f(x) = 2x^3 - 3x^2 + 6x - 1.$$

Then

$$
\begin{aligned}
f(x + \alpha) &= 2(x + \alpha)^3 - 3(x + \alpha)^2 + 6(x + \alpha) - 1 \\
&= 2(x^3 + 3x^2\alpha + 3x\alpha^2 + \alpha^3) \\
&\quad - 3(x^2 + 2x\alpha + \alpha^2) + 6(x + \alpha) - 1 \\
&= (2x^3 - 3x^2 + 6x - 1) + (6x^2 - 6x + 6)\alpha \\
&\quad\quad\quad\quad\quad\quad + (6x - 3)\alpha^2 + 2\alpha^3.
\end{aligned}
$$

So in this case

$$
\begin{aligned}
f_0(x) &= 2x^3 - 3x^2 + 6x - 1, \\
f_1(x) &= 6x^2 - 6x + 6, \\
f_2(x) &= 6x - 3, \\
f_3(x) &= 2.
\end{aligned}
$$

We see that the term $f_0(x)$ coincides with $f(x)$. This is not accidental. Equation (30) is an identity in x and α, and on putting $\alpha = 0$, as we may, we find that $f(x) = f_0(x)$.

We now concentrate our attention on the next term, $f_1(x)\alpha$. The coefficient of α, that is, the polynomial $f_1(x)$, is called the *derivative* of the polynomial $f(x)$. Thus we have shown that the derivative of $2x^3 - 3x^2 + 6x - 1$ is $6x^2 - 6x + 6$. The derivative of the polynomial $f(x)$ is usually written $f'(x)$.

Thus *the derivative $f'(x)$ of a polynomial $f(x)$ is defined as the coefficient of α in the expansion by powers of α of the polynomial $f(x + \alpha)$.*

Using our new notation, we can rewrite (30) in the form

$$f(x + \alpha) = f(x) + f'(x)\alpha + \ldots, \qquad (31)$$

where dots replace terms containing $\alpha^2, \ldots, \alpha^k$. For example,

$$
\begin{aligned}
2(x + \alpha)^3 &- 3(x + \alpha)^2 + 6(x + \alpha) - 1 \\
&= 2x^3 - 3x^2 + 6x - 1 + (6x^2 - 6x + 6)\alpha + \ldots
\end{aligned}
$$

We have introduced the concept of the derivative $f'(x)$ of a general polynomial function $f(x)$. We now proceed to calculate it knowing f. We consider the polynomial

$$f(x + \alpha) = a_0(x + \alpha)^k + a_1(x + \alpha)^{k-1} + \ldots + a_{k-1}(x + \alpha) + a_k.$$

Replacing each term by its expansion (22), we find that

$$f(x + \alpha) = a_0(x^k + kx^{k-1}\alpha + \ldots)$$
$$+ a_1[x^{k-1} + (k - 1)x^{k-2}\alpha^2 + \ldots] + \ldots$$
$$+ a_{k-1}(x + \alpha) + a_k$$
$$= a_0x^k + a_1x^{k-1} + \ldots + a_k$$
$$+ \alpha[ka_0x^{k-1} + (k - 1)a_1x^{k-2} + \ldots + a_{k-1}] + \ldots$$

Let us compare this with the equation (31):

$$f(x + \alpha) = f(x) + \alpha f'(x) + \ldots$$

We obtain the following result:

The derivative of the polynomial

$$f(x) = a_0x^k + a_1x^{k-1} + \ldots + a_{k-1}x + a_k \qquad (32)$$

is the polynomial

$$f'(x) = ka_0x^{k-1} + (k - 1)a_1x^{k-2} + \ldots + a^k_{-1}. \qquad (33)$$

For example, the derivative of the polynomial

$$f(x) = 6x^7 + 8x^3 - 3x^2 - 1$$

is

$$f'(x) = 42x^6 + 24x^2 - 6x.$$

8

NEWTON'S METHOD FOR THE APPROXIMATE SOLUTION OF ALGEBRAIC EQUATIONS

WE now consider the problem of approximating a root of an algebraic equation. Suppose we are given the equation

$$a_0 x^k + a_1 x^{k-1} + \ldots + a_k = 0. \tag{34}$$

We assume that by some method we have found an approximate value x_1 of a root of this equation, and we are to show how to find a better approximation. We denote by α_1 the error in the value x_1 for the root, so that the root is $x_1 + \alpha_1$. We then have the equation

$$a_0(x_1 + \alpha_1)^k + a_1(x_1 + \alpha_1)^{k-1} + \ldots + a_k = 0. \tag{35}$$

In other words,

$$f(x_1 + \alpha_1) = 0,$$

where $f(x)$ is the polynomial

$$a_0 x^k + a_1 x^{k-1} + \ldots + a_k.$$

But according to (31) we have

$$f(x_1 + \alpha_1) = f(x_1) + \alpha_1 f'(x_1) + \ldots,$$

where the dots, as usual, replace terms containing $\alpha_1^2, \ldots, \alpha_1^k$. Thus for the determination of α_1 we have the equation

$$f(x_1 + \alpha_1) = f(x_1) + \alpha_1 f'(x_1) + \ldots = 0. \tag{36}$$

If our initial approximation x_1 was good enough, then α_1 is small, and the sum of the missing terms in (36) will be small in comparison with α_1. If we neglect these terms, we obtain the approximation

$$f(x_1) + \alpha_1 f'(x_1) \approx 0 \tag{37}$$

for α_1. From this approximate equation we deduce that

$$\alpha_1 \approx -\frac{f(x_1)}{f'(x_1)}. \tag{38}$$

Thus we may obtain a better approximation x_2 to the root of our equation by means of the formula

$$x_2 = x_1 - \frac{f(x_1)}{f'(x_1)}. \tag{39}$$

We can now go a step further and obtain an even better approximation by taking

$$x_3 = x_2 - \frac{f(x_2)}{f'(x_2)}.$$

In general, suppose we have found an nth approximation x_n to the required root. Then we obtain a better approximation x_{n+1} by means of the formula

$$x_{n+1} = x_n - \frac{f(x_n)}{f'(x_n)}. \tag{40}$$

This formula may be expanded as

$$x_{n+1} = x_n - \frac{a_0 x_n^k + a_1 x_n^{k-1} + \ldots + a_{k-1} x_n + a_k}{k a_0 x_n^{k-1} + (k-1) a_1 x_n^{k-2} + \ldots + a_{k-1}}. \tag{41}$$

If we are required to calculate a root to within a certain accuracy, we need only carry out this process until x_n and x_{n+1} coincide to the appropriate number of decimal places. We will then have attained our solution.

This method of solving equations was developed by Newton.

EXAMPLE. Use Newton's method to find a root of the equation

$$x^3 - 3x - 5 = 0$$

to within 0.001, taking as a first approximation $x_1 = 3$.

Since the derivative of the polynomial

$$f(x) = x^3 - 3x - 5$$

is the polynomial

$$f'(x) = 3x^2 - 3,$$

formula (40) now takes the form

$$x_{n+1} = x_n - \frac{x_n^3 - 3x_n - 5}{3x_n^2 - 3}.$$

Therefore

$$x_2 = 3 - \frac{27 - 9 - 5}{27 - 3} = 3 - \frac{13}{24} = 2.46,$$

$$x_3 = 2.46 - \frac{14.89 - 7.38 - 5}{18.16 - 3} = 2.46 - 0.165 = 2.295,$$

$$x_4 = 2.295 - \frac{12.088 - 6.885 - 5}{15.801 - 3} = 2.295 - 0.016 = 2.279,$$

$$x_5 = 2.279 - \frac{11.837 - 6.807 - 5}{15.582 - 3} = 2.279.$$

We see that $x_4 = x_5$ to within 0.001, and therefore a root of the equation $x^3 - 3x - 5 = 0$ lies within 0.001 of 2.279.

The method we described in Chapter 6 for the approximate calculation of kth roots is a special case of Newton's method. As we have already pointed out, a process of determining $\sqrt[k]{a}$ is merely a process for solving the algebraic equation

$$x^k - a = 0.$$

Now the derivative of the polynomial $x^k - a$ is kx^{k-1}, and when formula (40) is applied to this problem, we see that

$$x_{n+1} = x_n - \frac{x_n^k - a}{kx_n^{k-1}} = \frac{a + (k-1)x_n^k}{kx_n^{k-1}}.$$

But this is precisely the formula (27) we used for calculating the successive approximations to $\sqrt[k]{a}$.

We note the following substantial difference between the process of solving the equation $x^k - a = 0$ and the process of solving a general algebraic equation

$$a_0 x^k + a_1 x^{k-1} + \ldots + a_k = 0.$$

For the equation $x^k - a = 0$ our choice of a first approximation x_1 is immaterial. Whatever value we choose for it, we will ultimately come as close as we like to $\sqrt[k]{a}$. This is by no means so when we try to find a root of equation (34). Here some initial choices will lead to one root, some to another, and certain initial choices will not lead to any root; that is, the sequence $x_1, x_2, \ldots, x_n, \ldots,$ will not tend to any definite value. In other words, the sequence will diverge. It is true, however, that if the sequence $x_1, x_2, \ldots, x_n, \ldots,$ calculated according to (40), does tend to a limit, then this limit will be a root of the equation $f(x) = 0$.

9

THE GEOMETRIC
INTERPRETATION OF THE
DERIVATIVE

WE have given an account of Newton's method only for polynomial functions. To generalize the method to a wider class of functions, we shall extend the concept of the derivative by clarifying the geometric significance of the derivative of a function.

Let us consider the graph of the polynomial

$$y = a_0 x^k + a_1 x^{k-1} + \ldots + a_k$$

and choose two points M and N on it. Suppose the abscissa at M is x and at N is $x + \alpha$. Then the ordinates at M and N are given by

$$f(x) = a_0 x^k + a_1 x^{k-1} + \ldots + a_k$$

and

$$f(x + \alpha) = a_0(x + \alpha)^k + a_1(x + \alpha)^{k-1} + \ldots + a_k.$$

Let us draw the secant through M and N, and calculate its slope k. This is defined as the tangent of the angle MN makes with the x-axis. If MN makes an angle of $60°$ with the x-axis, for example, its slope is $\sqrt{3}$. We see from Fig. 2 that

$$k = \tan \psi = \frac{TN}{MT}.$$

But the length of MT is equal to the difference between the abscissas of M and N, so that

$$MT = (x + \alpha) - x = \alpha.$$

Also TN is equal to the difference between their ordinates:

$$TN = f(x + \alpha) - f(x).$$

29

Thus

$$\tan \psi = \frac{TN}{MT} = \frac{f(x + \alpha) - f(x)}{\alpha}.$$

But by formula (31)

$$f(x + \alpha) = f(x) + \alpha f'(x) + \cdot \cdot \cdot,$$

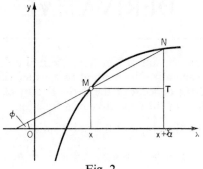

Fig. 2

where the dots stand for terms in α^2, α^3, . . . Thus

$$\tan \psi = \frac{\alpha f'(x) + \cdot \cdot \cdot}{\alpha} = f'(x) + \cdot \cdot \cdot,$$

where this time the dots stand for terms in α, α^2, . . .

Thus the slope of the secant MN is given by the formula

$$k_{\text{sec}} = \tan \psi = f'(x) + \cdot \cdot \cdot \tag{42}$$

We now make α smaller and smaller. As we do so the secant MN will turn about M (which remains fixed, of course). In the limit as α tends to zero, the secant will swing into coincidence with the tangent to the curve $y = f(x)$ at the point M. In Fig. 3 we show the positions of the secants for the values 1, $\frac{1}{2}$, $\frac{1}{4}$ of α, and also the tangent at M.

But as α tends to zero, the sum of all the terms in (42) which are represented by dots also tends to zero, since they all have a factor of α. Thus the slope of the tangent to the graph of the curve $y = f(x)$ at the point with abscissa x is given by the formula

$$K_{\text{tan}} = f'(x). \tag{43}$$

Note that the graph of a polynomial does have a tangent at every point.

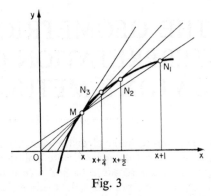

Fig. 3

EXAMPLE. Find the angle between the x-axis and the tangent to the graph of the equation

$$y = x^3 - 4x^2 + 5x + 1 = f(x)$$

at the point with abscissa $x = 2$.

Since
$$f'(x) = 3x^2 - 8x + 5,$$

we see that $f'(2) = 1$. Thus $\tan \varphi = 1$, so that φ, the limiting value of ψ, is equal to $45°$.

10

THE GEOMETRIC INTERPRETATION OF NEWTON'S METHOD

WE are now in a position to make clear the geometric interpretation of Newton's method for the approximate solution of algebraic equations. Suppose we are required to find a root of the equation $f(x) = 0$, where $f(x)$ is some polynomial. Geometrically, this is the problem of finding the points of intersection of the graph of the function $y = f(x)$ with the x-axis, that is, points at which $y = 0$.

Let us suppose that we already have an approximate value x_1 of a root of this equation. Let N be the point on the graph of the curve $y = f(x)$ whose abscissa is x_1, and suppose the tangent to the curve at N meets the x-axis at T. If our first choice x_1 was good, T will be closer to our root than M, the point with abscissa x_1 from which we started (see Fig. 4).

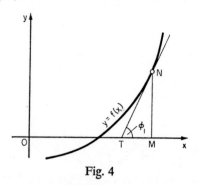

Fig. 4

To find the abscissa x_2 of the point T, let us consider the triangle TMN. The length of the vertical side MN is precisely the value of the function $y = f(x)$ at the point x_1; that is, $MN = f(x_1)$. The length of the horizontal side TM is $x_1 - x_2$. It follows that the tangent of

32

the angle φ_1 that TN makes with the x-axis is given by the expression

$$\tan \varphi_1 = \frac{f(x_1)}{x_1 - x_2}. \tag{44}$$

It follows from (44) that

$$x_2 = x_1 - \frac{f(x_1)}{\tan \varphi_1}. \tag{45}$$

But $\tan \varphi_1$ is the slope of the tangent to the curve $y = f(x)$ at the point with abscissa x_1. Thus, from the geometric interpretation of the derivative we see that $\tan \varphi_1 = f'(x_1)$.

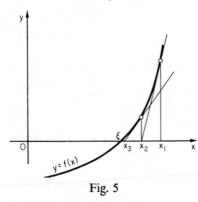

Fig. 5

So we may rewrite formula (45) as

$$x_2 = x_1 - \frac{f(x_1)}{f'(x_1)}.$$

We have thus found our second approximation for the required root. We now repeat the whole process, drawing a tangent to the curve at the point with abscissa x_2, and finding that it meets the x-axis at the point with abscissa x_3, where

$$x_3 = x_2 - \frac{f(x_2)}{f'(x_2)}.$$

In general, if we have already found an approximation x_n, then to find the next approximation x_{n+1} we draw the tangent to the curve at the point with abscissa x_n. The abscissa of the point of intersection of this line with the x-axis is the required next approximation x_{n+1}. It is given by

$$x_{n+1} = x_n - \frac{f(x_n)}{f'(x_n)} \qquad (46)$$

or, equivalently,

$$x_{n+1} = x_n - \frac{f(x_n)}{\tan \varphi_n}, \qquad (46')$$

where φ_n is the angle between the x-axis and the tangent to $y = f(x)$ at the point with abscissa x_n. This formula coincides with formula (40) for Newton's method. We have thus discovered the geometric significance of Newton's method. It amounts to our approximating the arc of the curve $y = f(x)$ between N and the required root by its tangent at N. We may therefore call Newton's method the *method of tangents*.

Figure 5 shows how the successive approximations $x_1, x_2, \ldots,$ $x_n, \ldots,$ obtained by Newton's method, approach the point ξ at which the curve $y = f(x)$ cuts the x-axis.

Note: In obtaining (45), and similarly (46), we assumed the graph of $y = f(x)$ was of the form shown in Fig. 4 (for example, we assumed $f(x_1)$ was positive and $x_1 > x_2$). Even if the graph is of a different form, however (see for example Fig. 7, p. 41), the formula (45) for the abscissa of the point of intersection of the tangent and the x-axis will hold (and (46) likewise). But it should be noted that x_{n+1} may in some cases be further from ξ than x_n is (see Fig. 7a, with $x_n = a$).

11

THE DERIVATIVE OF MORE GENERAL FUNCTIONS

OUR geometric interpretation of Newton's method of tangents had nothing to do with the assumption that $f(x)$ was a polynomial. We can, in fact, extend the method immediately to the solution of any equation $f(x) = 0$, provided the graph of the function $y = f(x)$ has a tangent at every point. To find a solution of the equation, we choose an approximate root x_1. At the point of the curve with abscissa x_1 we draw a tangent, and denote by x_2 the point at which it meets the x-axis. If the tangent is horizontal, of course, we cannot do this, but that merely means our first approximation was not good enough, and we have to choose a closer one. Having obtained x_2, we again draw the tangent to the curve $y = f(x)$, at the point with abscissa x_2. Continuing in this way, we obtain a sequence of approximations $x_1, x_2, \ldots, x_n, \ldots$, where we may establish, just as when we assumed $f(x)$ was a polynomial, that

$$x_{n+1} = x_n - \frac{f(x_n)}{\tan \varphi_n}, \tag{47}$$

where $\tan \varphi_n$ is the slope of the tangent to the curve $y = f(x)$ at the point with abscissa x_n.

Formula (47) is not enough for calculations, since we do not yet know how to compute $\tan \varphi_n$. We therefore need a method of calculating the slopes of the tangents to the graphs of *arbitrary* functions $y = f(x)$, and not only of polynomials. First, let us find the slope of a secant. Let M be a point on the graph of the curve $y = f(x)$ and MN a secant through it. Arguing as we did for polynomials, we find that the slope of this secant is given by the formula

$$k_{\text{sec}} = \tan \psi = \frac{f(x + \alpha) - f(x)}{\alpha}, \tag{48}$$

where x is the abscissa of the point M and $x + \alpha$ of N. If we decrease α, this secant will turn about M and tend towards the position

35

of the tangent to the curve at M. We may therefore write

$$k_{\tan} = \tan \varphi = \lim_{\alpha \to 0} \frac{f(x + \alpha) - f(x)}{\alpha}. \tag{49}$$

We call the limit on the right side the *derivative* of the function $f(x)$ at the point x, and denote it by $f'(x)$. The *derived function* (or simply the *derivative*) of the function f is the function f' whose value at the point x is $f'(x)$, that is,

$$f'(x) = \lim_{\alpha \to 0} \frac{f(x + \alpha) - f(x)}{\alpha}. \tag{50}$$

Of course, this function is only defined where the limit exists, but it can be proved that the limit does exist wherever the curve $y = f(x)$ has a tangent.

We may now rewrite equation (49) in the form

$$k_{\tan} = \tan \varphi = f'(x). \tag{51}$$

Thus for any function f, the derivative of f at a point is equal to the slope of the tangent to the curve $y = f(x)$ at that point (provided the tangent exists).

Since $\tan \varphi_n = f'(x_n)$, formula (47) may be rewritten

$$x_{n+1} = x_n - \frac{f(x_n)}{f'(x_n)}. \tag{52}$$

This formula coincides with formula (40). We have thus extended Newton's method to arbitrary equations $f(x) = 0$.

12

THE CALCULATION OF DERIVATIVES

WE saw in the last section that the slope of the tangent to a curve $y = f(x)$ at the point x is given by

$$f'(x) = \lim_{\alpha \to 0} \frac{f(x + \alpha) - f(x)}{\alpha}.$$

The calculation of this limit is, in general, rather difficult. The limit has been found in many important cases, however. In other words, the derived functions of the most familiar functions are known. We list the commonest:

1. $(a)' = 0.$

2. $(x^k)' = kx^{k-1}.$

3. $(a^x)' = a^x \ln a.$

4. $(\sin ax)' = a \cos ax.$

5. $(\cos ax)' = -a \sin ax.$

6. $(\tan ax)' = \dfrac{a}{\cos^2 ax}.$

7. $(\cot ax)' = -\dfrac{a}{\sin^2 ax}.$

8. $(\log_a x)' = \dfrac{1}{x \ln a}.$

9. $(\arcsin ax)' = \dfrac{a}{\sqrt{(1 - a^2 x^2)}}.$

10. $(\arctan ax)' = \dfrac{a}{1 + a^2 x^2}.$

In formulas 3 and 8 the logarithm is understood to be taken to base $e = 2.71828 \ldots$ (this is the so-called *natural* logarithm). In formula 2 the index k need not be a natural number, but can be any real number. Thus

$$(\sqrt{x})' = (x^{\frac{1}{2}})' = \tfrac{1}{2}x^{\frac{1}{2}-1} = \frac{1}{2\sqrt{x}},$$

$$\left(\frac{1}{x^2}\right)' = (x^{-2})' = -2x^{-3} = -\frac{2}{x^3}.$$

Formulas 1–10 do not suffice for the calculation of the derived function of many of the well-known functions. But if a function f is

37

constructed by means of arithmetic operations from functions whose derived functions are known, then we can calculate the derived function of f. To do so, we use the following rules, which, like formulas 1–10, are proved in courses of higher mathematics.

1. *The derivative of the sum function of two given functions is the sum function of their derivatives, that is,*

$$(f_1 + f_2)' = f_1' + f_2'.$$

2. *The derivative of the product of a constant and a function is the product of the constant and the derivative of the function*

$$(af)' = af'.$$

3. *The derivative of the product function of two functions is given by the formula*

$$(f_1 f_2)' = f_1' f_2 + f_1 f_2'.$$

4. *The derivative of the quotient of two functions is given by the formula*

$$\left[\frac{f_1}{f_2}\right]' = \frac{f_1' f_2 - f_1 f_2'}{f_2^2}.$$

The rule given in Chapter 7 for calculating the derivative of a polynomial is a consequence of rules 1 and 2 and formulas 1 and 2 in our list.

EXAMPLE 1. Find the derivative of the quotient

$$f(x) = \frac{3x^2 - x + 1}{2x^3 + 5}.$$

Using rule 4, we find that

$$f'(x) = \frac{(3x^2 - x + 1)'(2x^3 + 5) - (3x^2 - x + 1)(2x^3 + 5)'}{(2x^3 + 5)^2}.$$

Next, using the rule for differentiating a polynomial, we find that

$$(3x^2 - x + 1)' = 6x - 1$$

and

$$(2x^3 + 5)' = 6x^2,$$

and therefore

$$f'(x) = \frac{(2x^3 + 5)(6x - 1) - (3x^2 - x + 1)6x^2}{(2x^3 + 5)^2}$$

$$= \frac{-6x^4 + 4x^3 + 6x^2 + 30x - 5}{(2x^3 + 5)^2}.$$

38

THE CALCULATION OF DERIVATIVES

EXAMPLE 2. Find the derivative of the function

$$f(x) = \frac{1}{10}\left(\text{arc-sin } 3x - \frac{1}{x^2}\right).$$

Solution. Using formulas 2 and 9, and rules 1 and 2, we find that

$$f'(x) = \frac{1}{10}\frac{3}{\sqrt{(1-9x^2)}} - \frac{1}{10}\left(\frac{-2}{x^3}\right) = \frac{3}{10\sqrt{(1-9x^2)}} + \frac{1}{5x^3}.$$

EXAMPLE 3. Find the derivative of the function

$$f(x) = 10^x \sin 2x.$$

Using rule 3 and formulas 3 and 4, we find that

$$\begin{aligned}
f'(x) &= (10^x)' \sin 2x + 10^x (\sin 2x)' \\
&= 10^x \sin 2x \ln 10 + 10^x \cdot 2 \cos 2x \\
&= 10^x (\sin 2x \ln 10 + 2 \cos 2x).
\end{aligned}$$

The rules we have given allow us to find the derivatives of a large number of functions. There is one further important rule—the rule for calculating the derivative of a composite function.

5. *If the function $y = f(x)$ can be written in the form $y = F(z)$, where $z = \varphi(x)$, then its derivative is given by*

$$f'(x) = F'(z)\varphi'(x), \tag{53}$$

where $z = \varphi(x)$.

EXAMPLE. Find the derivatives of the function $y = \sin(x^3)$. This function can be written in the form $y = \sin z$, where $z = x^3$. The derivative of the function $F(z) = \sin z$ is $F'(z) = \cos z$, and the derivative of the function $\varphi(x) = x^3$ is $\varphi'(x) = 3x^2$. Using formula (53) we find that

$$[\sin(x^3)]' = F'(z)\varphi'(x) = \cos z \cdot 3x^2.$$

Substituting the value x^3 for z, we find that

$$[\sin(x^3)]' = 3x^2 \cos x^3.$$

A more detailed discussion of the concept of a derivative may be found in any good calculus textbook.

13

FINDING A FIRST APPROXIMATION

WE now consider the selection of a first approximation to a root of our equation $f(x) = 0$. This may be done graphically by sketching the graph $y = f(x)$ and seeing where it meets the x-axis. Since $y = 0$ at these points, they will be roots of the equation. The accuracy of the first approximation will depend on the accuracy of our graph.

If for some reason it is inconvenient to graph the function, we may use another method. With this method we calculate the values of the function for certain values of x (for example the integers in a certain range). If $y = f(x)$ is continuous (if its graph has no

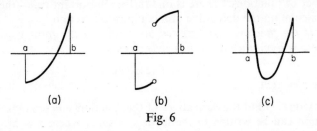

(a)   (b)   (c)

Fig. 6

breaks), then between any two values a and b at which the function has opposite signs there will be a root of the equation $f(x) = 0$ (see Fig. 6a). If the graph has breaks, this may be false (Fig. 6b). We may take a or b as our first approximation.

Let us note that we may miss a number of roots if we use this method. Thus in Fig. 6c we give an example of a function that has the same sign at a and b, and yet has a root (actually two roots) in between.

At any rate, suppose we now have the two points a and b at which the function has opposite signs. Which is it better to take as our first approximation? On considering Fig. 7a and b we conclude that if the graph of the function is concave upward between a and b, the better first approximation is the one at which f is positive. If we

40

choose the other point, our second approximation might even land outside the interval [*a*, *b*]. On considering Fig. 7c and d, we see in the same way that if the graph is concave downward, we should choose the point at which *f* is negative.

Let us note here that we are talking about the best *first* approximation to a root of $f(x) = 0$ so far as Newton's method is concerned.

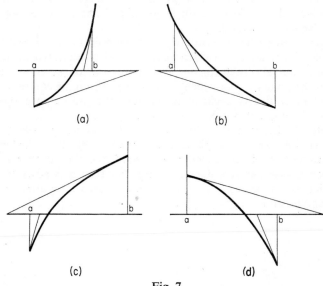

(a)   (b)

(c)   (d)

Fig. 7

It can easily happen that when choosing between *a* and *b*, the point *a* which is closest to the root ξ will not yield as desirable a first approximation as the point *b* which is further away from the root ξ.

This rule for choosing between *a* and *b* is useful when we have a graph of the function in front of us. If, however, we have no graph, we need some other method to determine whether the graph is concave upward or downward. To do so we must calculate the second derivative of the function $f(x)$. *The second derivative of a function $f(x)$ is the derivative of its first derivative.* If we are given the function

$$f(x) = x^3 - 4x^2 + 3x - 1,$$

we find that its derivative is

$$f'(x) = 3x^2 - 8x + 3,$$

41

and therefore its second derivative is

$$f''(x) = 6x - 8.$$

In advanced mathematics it is proved that if the second derivative of f is positive throughout the interval $[a, b]$, then the graph of f is concave upward in this interval, and if it is negative throughout the interval, then f is concave downward. Using this fact, we obtain the following rule for deciding on a first approximation when we are using Newton's method.

Suppose that f has opposite signs at the points a and b and that the second derivative of f (which we assume exists) is positive throughout this interval. Then for our first approximation we choose that one of the points a, b at which f is positive. If, on the contrary, the second derivative is negative throughout the interval, we should choose the point at which f is negative.

Note, finally, that f might well be neither concave upward nor concave downward throughout the interval $[a, b]$. It might begin, for example, by being concave downward and then change over. In such a case our rule does not help, but then it is advisable to calculate the value of f at $c = \frac{1}{2}(a + b)$, and restrict our attention to the subinterval $([a, c]$ or $[c, b])$ in which f changes sign.

14

THE METHOD OF CHORDS

WE now describe a different method, the method of chords, for solving equations approximately. Suppose, as in the previous section, that we have already found points a and b at which f has opposite signs. As we have said, if f is continuous, the equation $f(x) = 0$ has a root between a and b. That is, there is at least one point where the graph $y = f(x)$ crosses the x-axis. To obtain an

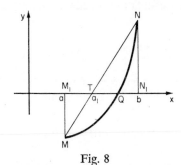

Fig. 8

approximation to this point, we replace the arc of the curve $y = f(x)$ lying between a and b by the chord MN (see Fig. 8), and find the point T where this chord meets the x-axis.

To find the point T we consider the similar triangles MM_1T and NN_1T. It follows from their similarity that $M_1T/MM_1 = TN_1/N_1N$. But it is clear from Fig. 8 that $M_1T = a_1 - a$, $TN_1 = b - a_1$, $MM_1 = -f(a)$, and $N_1N = f(b)$, where a_1 is the abscissa of T. Thus we have

$$\frac{a_1 - a}{-f(a)} = \frac{b - a_1}{f(b)}.$$

On solving this equation for a_1, we find that

$$a_1 = \frac{af(b) - bf(a)}{f(b) - f(a)}.$$

43

This equation may be written

$$a_1 = b - f(b)\frac{b-a}{f(b)-f(a)} \tag{54}$$

or

$$a_1 = a - f(a)\frac{b-a}{f(b)-f(a)}. \tag{55}$$

The value a_1 is taken as our second approximation to the root (or one of the roots) of $f(x) = 0$ lying between a and b.

Since f has opposite sign at a and b, the sign of $f(a_1)$ must differ from at least one of them. The only other possibility is that $f(a_1) = 0$, but in that case we have found the exact root and there is no need to go further. Suppose then that f has opposite sign at a and a_1. Then we apply formula (54) to the segment $[a, a_1]$ and find the approximation

$$a_2 = a_1 - f(a_1)\frac{a_1-a}{f(a_1)-f(a)}$$

for the required root. If f has opposite sign at a_1 and b, we apply the formula (55) to the segment $[a_1, b]$ and find

$$a_2 = a_1 - f(a_1)\frac{b-a_1}{f(b)-f(a_1)}.$$

Having found the value of a_2, say between a and a_1, we see whether the sign of $f(a_2)$ differs from that of $f(a)$ or $f(a_1)$. If, say, the latter, we continue as before, but taking a_2 and a_1 as the end points of our interval (instead of a and b). In general, we shall find at the nth stage that there is a root of the equation $f(x) = 0$ between c and a_n (where c is either some previous a_i or the point a) or between a_n and d (where d is either a previous a_i or the point b). We then apply our original procedure, starting with the interval $[c, a_n]$ (or $[a_n, d]$), to obtain a new point a_{n+1} inside the interval. Thus our sequence of approximation yields us a "nested" sequence of intervals, and this will, in general, converge to a single point, the required root.

We now consider two useful special cases of this procedure. Suppose first that throughout the interval $[a, b]$ the graph of f either decreases steadily and is concave upwards (as in Fig. 9a) or increases steadily and is concave downwards (Fig. 9b). Then we easily see that the left-hand end point of each interval of our nested

44

sequence is the point a, and the right-hand end point a_n is given recursively by the formula

$$a_{n+1} = a_n - f(a_n) \frac{a_n - a}{f(a_n) - f(a)}. \tag{56}$$

Similarly, if the graph of f is of one of the types shown in Fig. 9c and d, the right-hand end point of each of the intervals of our

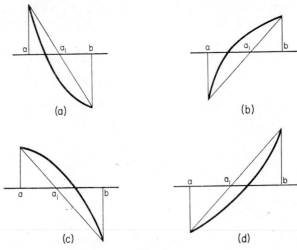

(a)

(b)

(c)

(d)

Fig. 9

nested sequence is the point b and the left-hand end point is given recursively by the formula

$$a_{n+1} = a_n - f(a_n) \frac{b - a_n}{f(b) - f(a_n)}. \tag{57}$$

The method of chords may profitably be used in combination with Newton's method. Thus we start by calculating a_1 by means of formula (55), and x_1 by means of the formula

$$x_1 = b - \frac{f(b)}{f'(b)} \tag{58}$$

or

$$x_1 = a - \frac{f(a)}{f'(a)},$$

according to the end of the segment $[a, b]$ at which the sign of f

coincides with that of its second derivative. As we see from Fig. 10a and b, the root ξ of the equation $f(x) = 0$ will lie between the points a_1 and x_1. At least, this will be true so long as the graph is of one of the forms shown in Fig. 9. We start again, now, with the points a_1 and x_1, and use them to obtain a further pair, a_2, x_2.

Working in this way, we find two sequences $a_1, a_2, \ldots, a_n, \ldots,$ and $x_1, x_2, \ldots, x_n, \ldots,$ converging to the required root from opposite sides. This method has the advantage that we know at each stage the limits of accuracy of our calculated value of the root.

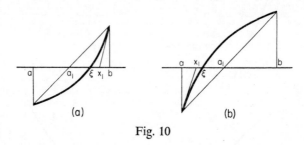

(a)　　　　　　　　(b)

Fig. 10

We know at stage n that the root lies between a_n and x_n, and therefore that a value $\frac{1}{2}|a_n + x_n|$ cannot be more than $\frac{1}{2}|a_n - x_n|$ off.

EXAMPLE. Use the combined method to calculate a root of the equation

$$x - \sin x - 0.5 = 0$$

to within 0.001.

We compile a table of values of the continuous function

$$f(x) = x - \sin x - 0.5$$

x	-1	0	1	2
$f(x)$	-0.659	-0.5	-0.341	0.591

We see from this table that there is a root of the equation between 1 and 2. Using formulas 1, 2, and 4 of Chapter 12, we find that

$$f'(x) = 1 - \cos x.$$

46

Thus in our case Newton's formula assumes the form

$$x_{n+1} = x_n - \frac{x_n - \sin x_n - 0.5}{1 - \cos x_n}. \tag{59}$$

To determine whether we should take 1 or 2 for x_0, we find the second derivative of f. Using formulas 1 and 5 of Chapter 12, we find that $f''(x) = \sin x$. But the function $\sin x$ is positive throughout this interval, since 1 and 2 both lie within the interval $[0, \pi]$, and $\sin x$ is positive on this larger interval. So, by the rule stated earlier, we must take $x_0 = 2$, since f as well as f'' is positive there. By (59) we find that

$$x_1 = 2 - \frac{2 - \sin 2 - 0.5}{1 - \cos 2} = 2 - \frac{2 - 0.909 - 0.5}{1 + 0.416} = 1.583.$$

On the other hand, we find from (55) that

$$a_1 = 1 - (-0.341)\frac{2 - 1}{0.591 - (-0.341)} = 1.366.$$

Applying formulas (59) and (55) to the segment $[a_1, x_1]$, we find that

$$x_2 = 1.583 - \frac{1.583 - 1.000 - 0.5}{1 + 0.012} = 1.501$$

and

$$a_2 = 1.366 + 0.113\frac{1.583 - 1.366}{0.083 + 0.113} = 1.491.$$

Continuing, we find that

$$x_3 = 1.498,$$
$$a_3 = 1.498.$$

Thus a root of our equation is, to an accuracy of 0.001, equal to 1.498.

15

THE METHOD OF ITERATION

WE now consider a general method for the approximate solution of equations. We shall see that both Newton's method and the method of chords are special cases of this method, which is called the *method of iteration*, or the *method of successive approximation*. We start by examining this method as applied to a concrete example.

EXAMPLE. Find a root of the equation

$$10x - 1 - \cos x = 0 \tag{60}$$

accurate to within 0.001.

We rewrite the equation (60)

$$x = \frac{1 + \cos x}{10}. \tag{61}$$

We now choose some initial approximation, say $x_1 = 0$, and substitute it for x in the right side, but not the left side, of equation (61). This gives an equation for x whose value we take as our second approximation to a root; that is, we take

$$x_2 = \frac{1 + \cos 0}{10} = 0.2.$$

Substituting x_2 in the same way in the right side of (61), we obtain our third approximation

$$x_3 = \frac{1 + \cos 0.2}{10} \approx \frac{1 + 0.98}{10} = 0.198.$$

Continuing, we obtain

$$x_4 = \frac{1 + \cos 0.198}{10} \approx 0.198.$$

We see that $x_3 = x_4$ to within 0.001. Since $x_4 = (1 + \cos x_3)/10$ $x_3 = 0.198$ is a root of equation (61) to within 0.001.

The method we have described for solving equation (61) is that of iteration. In general we may describe the method as follows:

We write the equation $f(x) = 0$ in the form $x = \varphi(x)$. Then we select an initial approximation x_1, substitute in the right side of the equation, and obtain a second approximation $x_2 = \varphi(x_1)$. In general, if we have an approximation x_n, we obtain the next approximation x_{n+1} by means of the formula

$$x_{n+1} = \varphi(x_n). \tag{62}$$

If we find that to within the required accuracy $x_{n+1} = x_n$ we may take x_n for our root.

Newton's method is a special case of the method of iteration, because the method may be presented as follows.

Suppose we are given the equation $f(x) = 0$. We divide both sides by $-f'(x)$ and add x. We obtain

$$x = x - \frac{f(x)}{f'(x)}.$$

This equation is clearly equivalent to the original one, except possibly at those points where $f'(x) = 0$, where it is not defined. It turns out, however, that in a certain sense, which we shall not investigate here, this "almost never" matters.

Applying the method of iteration to this equation, we find that the successive approximations x_{n+1} are given by

$$\{x_{n+1}\} = x_n - \frac{f(x_n)}{f'(x_n)}.$$

But this is precisely the formula used in Newton's method.

In the same way we may show that the method of chords is a special case of the method of iteration. We may rewrite the equation $f(x) = 0$ in the form

$$x = x - f(x) \frac{x - a}{f(x) - f(a)}$$

or in the form

$$x = x - f(x) \frac{b - x}{f(b) - f(x)}.$$

A number of questions arise in connection with the method of iteration we have described:

1. Does the sequence $x_1, \ldots, x_n, \ldots$, obtained by the method of iteration always converge to some number ξ?

2. If it does, then is ξ a root of the equation $x = \varphi(x)$?

3. How rapidly does the sequence $x_1, \ldots, x_n, \ldots$, tend to a root ξ of the equation $x = \varphi(x)$?

The easiest question to answer is the second. Suppose the sequence $x_1, \ldots, x_n, \ldots$, tends to the limit ξ. Consider the equation

$$x_{n+1} = \varphi(x_n)$$

giving each term of the sequence by means of its predecessor. As n increases, the left side tends to ξ and if φ is continuous the right side tends to $\varphi(\xi)$. Thus in the limit we have $\xi = \varphi(\xi)$, which is to say that ξ is a root of the equation $x = \varphi(x)$.

The answer to the first question is negative. As an example we may take the problem of Achilles and the antelope (Chapter 3), where the method of iteration applied to equation (8) (see equation (9)), leads to the divergent sequence 0, 100, 300, 500. . . . There can be no limit, since the successive terms increase without bound. Notice, however, that if we rewrite equation (8) in the form $x = \frac{1}{2}(x - 100)$ and take $x_0 = 0$, then the method does lead to the correct solution $x = -100$. The first few terms are $0, -50, -75, -87.5, -93.75. \ldots$

Another example is given by the equation

$$x = 10^x - 2.$$

If we let $x_1 = 1$, then

$$x_2 = 8, x_3 = 10^8 - 2 \ldots$$

As n increases, x_n increases without bound. But if we rewrite this equation as

$$x = \log(x + 2),$$

then the approximating sequence converges, and after three approximations we find that $x = 2.38$ to two decimal places.

We should therefore rephrase our first question: "What sort of function φ should we choose in order for the sequence $x_1, \ldots, x_n, \ldots$, to converge?"

Our answer to question 2 shows that it is natural for us to restrict our attention to cases where φ is continuous, and this we shall do. Before attempting to go further into the question, we examine the geometric interpretation of the method of iteration.

16

THE GEOMETRIC
INTERPRETATION OF THE
METHOD OF ITERATION

FINDING a root ξ of the equation $x = \varphi(x)$ is clearly the same as finding the abscissa of a point M at which the curve $y = \varphi(x)$ and the straight line $y = x$ meet. Suppose we start with some initial approximation x_1 to ξ (Fig. 11a and b). Then the point M_1 with coordinates $(x_1, \varphi(x_1))$ lies on the curve $y = \varphi(x)$. We now draw the horizontal line through it, to meet the straight line $y = x$ at the point

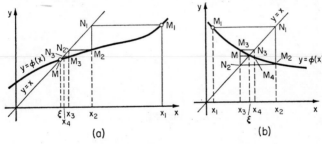

(a)   (b)

Fig. 11

$N_1(\varphi(x_1), \varphi(x_1))$. We denote $\varphi(x_1)$ by x_2. Then the coordinates of N_1 are (x_2, x_2). We now draw the vertical line through N_1. It meets the curve $y = \varphi(x)$ at the point $M_2 (x_2, \varphi(x_2))$. Continuing the process, we obtain the point N_2 on the line $y = x$ with coordinates (x_3, x_3), where $x_3 = \varphi(x_2)$, and then the point M_3 with coordinates $(x_3, \varphi(x_3))$, and so on. If the approximating process converges then the sequence of points $M_1, M_2, \ldots$, will converge to the point M of intersection of the line and the graph of $y = \varphi(x)$.

Thus the geometric interpretation of the method of iteration is that we move toward some point of intersection of the curve and the line along a broken path whose vertices lie on the curve and the line alternately, and whose sides are alternately horizontal and vertical (Fig. 11a).

If the curve and the line bear the sort of relationship to each other that is shown in Fig. 11a, then this broken line looks like a staircase (at least, as soon as we have come sufficiently close to M). On the other hand, if the curve and the line are disposed as in Fig. 11b, the broken line looks like a spiral.

If the process of iteration diverges (as in the problem of Achilles and the antelope), the steps of our staircase or spiral will become ever bigger, and the points $M_1, M_2, \ldots$, will recede from M instead of converging towards it (Fig. 12a and b).

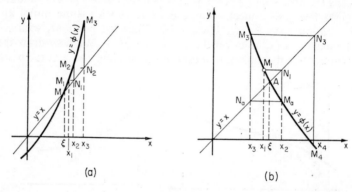

Fig. 12

We see from Fig. 11a and b that if the angle of inclination of the tangent to our curve at the point M lies between $-45°$ and $+45°$, and if our first approximation is reasonably close to M, then the sequence of points $M_1, M_2, \ldots$, will converge to M. If we choose M_1 too far to the right, we may "come under the influence" of the next point of intersection after M, or even more complicated things may happen. At any rate, in the case we are considering the slope of our curve at the point M (ξ, ξ) lies between -1 and 1. That is, $|\varphi'(\xi)| < 1$. If the angle of inclination of the tangent at M is greater than $45°$ or less than $-45°$ (Fig. 12a and b), the points $M_1, M_2, M_3, \ldots$, will get further and further from M. (They may not tend to the next point of intersection, however.) In this case either

$\varphi'(\xi) > 1$ or $\varphi'(\xi) < -1$. These two inequalities may be written compactly in the form

$$|\varphi'(\xi)| > 1.$$

Thus if φ has a derivative a sufficient condition for the method of iteration to work is that at the root ξ of the equation we have $|\varphi'(\xi)| < 1$. If the condition is satisfied, the sequence of approximations will converge provided only the first approximation is sufficiently close. If the condition is not satisfied, no choice of a first approximation, unless it is *exactly* the root, will lead to a sequence of approximations converging to ξ, though they may converge to some other root of the equation. We may say intuitively that the points of intersection where $|\varphi'(\xi)| < 1$ pull the broken line of the sequence of approximations towards them, and the points where $|\varphi'(\xi)| > 1$ drive it away.†

Since we do not know beforehand the exact value of ξ, this rule as it stands has no practical use. It may be proved, however, that if $|\varphi'(x)| < 1$ throughout the interval $[a, b]$, then there is at most one root of the equation $x = \varphi(x)$ on this interval, and if there is one, then any choice of a first approximation which lies in $[a, b]$ will lead to the root upon applying the method of iteration.

EXAMPLE 1. Can the process of iteration be applied to find a root of the equation

$$x = \frac{\cos x + \sin x}{4}?$$

Here we have

$$\varphi(x) = \frac{\cos x + \sin x}{4}.$$

Thus

$$\varphi'(x) = \frac{-\sin x + \cos x}{4}.$$

† Note that if the tangent to $y = \varphi(x)$ at $x = \xi$ makes an angle of $45°$ or $-45°$ with the x-axis, that is, $|\varphi'(\xi)| = 1$, then the sequence obtained may either converge or diverge. To illustrate this we give two examples for which $|\varphi'(\xi)| = 1$, but with one sequence converging and the other diverging.

If we try to solve the equation $x = \sin x$ by successive approximation we will succeed with any initial approximation. The sequence of approximation will converge to 0. But if we try to solve the equation $x^2 = 0$ by writing it in the form $x = x^2 + x$, the sequence obtained diverges for any first approximation except $x_1 = 0$. In both cases $|\varphi'(\xi)| = 1$.

But
$$|\sin x| \leqslant 1, \ |\cos x| \leqslant 1,$$

so that
$$|\varphi'(x)| = \left| \frac{-\sin x + \cos x}{4} \right|$$
$$\leqslant \frac{|\sin x| + |\cos x|}{4} \leqslant \frac{1}{2} \text{ for all } x,$$

and, by what we stated above, the equation has at most one root, and any choice of a first approximation will yield a sequence tending to it. To see that there does exist a root, notice that for large negative values of x we have $\varphi(x) > x$, while for large positive values of x we have $x > \varphi(x)$. Thus the continuous curve $y = \varphi(x)$ starts off above the line $y = x$, and ends up under it, and since φ is continuous, it must cross at some point.

EXAMPLE 2. Can the method of iteration be applied to solve the equation

$$x = 4 - 2^x? \tag{63}$$

We note first that this equation has exactly one root. Consider the graph of the function $y = x + 2^x - 4$. It is clear that the graph increases steadily, and is negative for large negative values of x and positive for large positive values. Thus the graph must cross the x-axis (at which point there is a root of the equation), and it cannot cross it more than once, since the function is steadily increasing. Now our root must lie between 1 and 2, for

$$1 < 4 - 2^1 = 2 \quad \text{while} \quad 2 > 4 - 2^2 = 0.$$

We therefore confine our attention to the segment $[1, 2]$. On this segment we have

$$\varphi'(x) = -2^x \ln 2,$$

where $1 \leqslant x \leqslant 2$, so that $2 \leqslant 2^x \leqslant 4$, and

$$2 \ln 2 \leqslant 2^x \ln 2 \leqslant 4 \ln 2.$$

Using tables of natural logarithms (to base $e = 2.78 \ldots$), we find that $\ln 2 = 0.69. \ldots$ So on the interval $[1, 2]$ we have

$$1.38 \ldots \leqslant 2^x \ln 2 \leqslant 2.76 \ldots,$$

and the process of iteration cannot be applied.

To be able to apply it, we rewrite equation (63) in another form. We begin by writing

$$2^x = 4 - x$$

and then take logarithms to base 2 of both sides. We find

$$x = \log_2 (4 - x).$$

For our new function φ we find that

$$\varphi'(x) = - \frac{1}{(4 - x) \ln 2},$$

so that on the segment [1, 2] we have the inequality

$$|\varphi'(x)| < \frac{1}{2 \ln 2} = \frac{1}{1.38} < 1.$$

The reader may easily prove this inequality.

Thus when the equation is written in this form, the sequence of approximations will converge.

17

THE SPEED OF CONVERGENCE OF A SEQUENCE OF SUCCESSIVE APPROXIMATIONS†

WE now give an estimate for the speed with which a sequence of successive approximations converges, that is, the speed with which the successive errors $\alpha_n = \xi - x_n$ tend to zero. We shall need a formula known as the mean value formula.

Consider the function $y = f(x)$ defined on a segment $[a, b]$, and suppose it has a derivative throughout this interval. Suppose M is

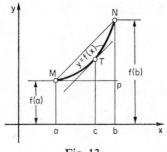

Fig. 13

the first and N the last point of the graph of this function. Then the slope of the chord MN is given by

$$k_{\text{chord}} = \tan \psi = \frac{PN}{MP}$$

(Fig. 13). But $MP = b - a$, and $PN = f(b) - f(a)$, and therefore

$$k_{\text{chord}} = \frac{f(b) - f(a)}{b - a}.$$

Suppose T is a point of the arc MN lying at the maximum possible

† This section may be omitted on first reading.

distance from the chord MN. If we draw a parallel through T to MN, it will be the tangent at T, for otherwise it would cross the arc, so that there would be a point of the arc further than T from MN. In other words, the tangent at T is parallel to MN and therefore has the same slope. But the slope of the tangent at T is $f'(c)$, where c is the abscissa of T. We thus have the formula

$$f'(c) = \frac{f(b) - f(a)}{b - a}. \tag{64}$$

This is the mean value formula. We note that the point c always lies strictly between a and b. The formula can also be written

$$f(b) - f(a) = f'(c)(b - a). \tag{65}$$

We return now to solving the equation $x = \varphi(x)$ by the method of iteration, and we suppose that φ has a derivative everywhere. Let ξ be the required root of the equation, and $x_1, \ldots, x_n, \ldots$ the sequence obtained by applying the method of iteration to an initial approximation x_1. We then have the equations $\xi = \varphi(\xi)$ and $x_{n+1} = \varphi(x_n)$. It follows from them that

$$\alpha_{n+1} = \xi - x_{n+1} = \varphi(\xi) - \varphi(x_n).$$

But by the mean value formula

$$\varphi(\xi) - \varphi(x_n) = \varphi'(c_n)(\xi - x_n) = \varphi'(c_n)\alpha_n,$$

where, for each n, c_n is a point lying between x_n and ξ. Thus

$$\alpha_{n+1} = \varphi'(c_n)\alpha_n. \tag{66}$$

From equation (66) we make the following deduction:

Let ξ be a root of the equation $x = \varphi(x)$ in the interval $[a, b]$. If throughout this interval we have the inequality $|\varphi'(x)| < q < 1$, and our first approximation x_1 is chosen in the interval, then for every n we have the inequality

$$|\alpha_{n+1}| < q^n |\alpha_1|. \tag{67}$$

It follows from (66) that

$$|\alpha_2| = |\varphi'(c_1)||\alpha_1|.$$

But c_1 lies inside the interval (see Fig. 14), and therefore

$$|\varphi'(c_1)| < q.$$

It follows from this that

$$|\alpha_2| < q|\alpha_1|.$$

Similarly, we find that

$$|\alpha_3| = |\varphi'(c_2)||\alpha_2| < q|\alpha_2| < q^2|\alpha_1|,$$

and, in general,

$$|\alpha_{n+1}| < q^n|\alpha_1|.$$

We have thus proved our assertion.

Since whenever $0 < q < 1$ the sequence $q, q^2, \ldots, q^n, \ldots$ tends to zero, the successive errors α_{n+1} will also tend to zero as n increases. In other words, under the conditions given above, the sequence of

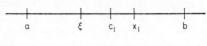

Fig. 14

approximations $x_1, \ldots, x_n, \ldots$ will always converge to ξ, and the successive errors $|\xi - x_{n+1}|$ will decrease faster than the terms of the geometric sequence $\{|\alpha_1|q^n : n = 0, 1, 2, \ldots\}$.

We can show in the same way that if throughout the interval $[a, b]$ we have the inequality

$$|\varphi'(x)| > 1,$$

then the sequence obtained by a process of iteration will diverge. A geometric discussion was given in Chapter 16.

The process of iteration converges especially rapidly if the derivative of φ is zero at ξ. In that case (assuming that the derivative of φ is continuous, as it almost always will be), $\varphi'(x)$ tends to zero as x tends to ξ. But since

$$|\alpha_{n+1}| = |\varphi'(c_n)||\alpha_n|$$

and c_n tends to ξ, the rate of convergence will increase as we approach ξ.

We have met this phenomenon in our consideration of an iterative method of extracting square roots (Chapter 5). We recall that we there replace the equation $x^2 = a$ by the equation $x = \dfrac{(x^2 + a)}{2x}$. But the derivative of the function $\varphi(x) = \dfrac{(x^2 + a)}{2x} = \dfrac{1}{2}x + \dfrac{a}{2}x^{-1}$ is the function

$$\varphi'(x) = \frac{1}{2} + \frac{a}{2} \cdot (-1)x^{-2}$$

(see rules 1 and 2 and formula 2 in Chapter 12). Thus

$$\varphi'(\sqrt{a}) = \frac{1}{2} + \frac{a}{2} \cdot (-1)\frac{1}{(\sqrt{a})^2} = 0.$$

So at the root $x = \sqrt{a}$ of our equation the derivative of the function φ is zero, and this is why the process of approximation continues to accelerate as we approach the solution.

This phenomenon of speeding up as we continue the process of approximation is typical of Newton's method, of which our process for extracting square roots was a special case. We have seen that Newton's method amounts to applying the method of iteration to the equation $f(x) = 0$ as rewritten in the form

$$x = x - \frac{f(x)}{f'(x)}.$$

Here we have

$$\varphi(x) = x - \frac{f(x)}{f'(x)}.$$

But

$$\varphi'(x) = 1 - \left[\frac{f(x)}{f'(x)} \right]' = 1 - \frac{f'(x)[f(x)]' - f(x)[f'(x)]'}{[f'(x)]^2}$$

$$= 1 - \frac{[f'(x)]^2 - f(x)f''(x)}{[f'(x)]^2} = \frac{f(x)f''(x)}{[f'(x)]^2}.$$

Since $f(\xi) = 0$, we also have $\varphi'(\xi) = 0$. And, as we have said, this is sufficient to make the approximating process speed up as we approach ξ.

18

THE SOLUTION OF A SYSTEM OF LINEAR EQUATIONS BY SUCCESSIVE APPROXIMATION

So far we have considered the solution of equations having only one unknown. We now consider the solution of systems of equations, confining our attention to systems of the first degree. Suppose we are given m equations of the first degree, in the m unknowns x_1, $x_2, \ldots, x_m$:

$$\left.\begin{aligned}
a_{11}x_1 + a_{12}x_2 + \ldots + a_{1m}x_m &= b_1, \\
a_{21}x_1 + a_{22}x_2 + \ldots + a_{2m}x_m &= b_2, \\
\cdots \cdots \cdots \cdots \cdots \cdots \\
a_{m1}x_1 + a_{m2}x_2 + \ldots + a_{mm}x_m &= b_m.
\end{aligned}\right\} \tag{68}$$

Here the a_{ij} are constants (i refers to the number of the equation, and j to the number of the unknown). For example, a_{24} is the coefficient of x_4 in the second equation. Such systems of linear equations are met with in many applications—in constructing accurate maps for large portions of the earth's surface (geodesy) or in engineering for estimating the strains and forces on systems of interlinked rods (for example, in the construction of a bridge or an airplane wing).

Solutions of such systems by ordinary methods, such as the successive elimination of unknowns, is tedious. It is often easier to use a process of successive approximation. We shall start by giving an example of how such a process can be applied.

Suppose we are given the system of equations

$$\left.\begin{aligned}
10x_1 - 2x_2 + x_3 &= 9 \\
x_1 + 5x_2 - x_3 &= 8 \\
4x_1 + 2x_2 + 8x_3 &= 39
\end{aligned}\right\}.$$

We are to find the values of x_1, x_2, x_3 to within 0.01.

We take x_1 to the other side of the first equation, x_2 in the second, and x_3 in the third, to obtain the rewritten system

$$\left.\begin{aligned} x_1 &= 0.9 + && 0.2x_2 - 0.1x_3 \\ x_2 &= 1.6 - 0.2x_1 + && 0.2x_3 \\ x_3 &= 4 - 0.5x_1 - 0.25x_2 \end{aligned}\right\}. \tag{69}$$

We choose an arbitrary set of values as our initial approximations, for example $x_1^{(0)} = 0$, $x_2^{(0)} = 0$, $x_3^{(0)} = 0$. We substitute these values in the right side of the system (69) and take the resulting values as our next approximations to the three unknowns. Thus we find that

$$x_1^{(1)} = 0.9,$$
$$x_2^{(1)} = 1.6,$$
$$x_3^{(1)} = 4.$$

These new values are now inserted in the right side of (69). We obtain the approximations

$$x_1^{(2)} = 0.9 + 0.2 \cdot 1.6 - 0.1 \cdot 4 = 0.82,$$
$$x_2^{(2)} = 1.6 - 0.2 \cdot 0.9 + 0.2 \cdot 4 = 2.22,$$
$$x_3^{(2)} = 4 - 0.5 \cdot 0.9 - 0.25 \cdot 1.6 = 3.15.$$

In general, if we have found a set of nth approximations $x_1^{(n)}$, $x_2^{(n)}$, $x_3^{(n)}$, then as our set of $(n + 1)$st approximations we take the values given by the formulas

$$\left.\begin{aligned} x_1^{(n+1)} &= 0.9 + 0.2x_2^{(n)} - 0.1x_3^{(n)}, \\ x_2^{(n+1)} &= 1.6 - 0.2x_1^{(n)} + 0.2x_3^{(n)}, \\ x_3^{(n+1)} &= 4 - 0.5x_1^{(n)} - 0.25x_2^{(n)}. \end{aligned}\right\} \tag{70}$$

The results of our successive calculations are shown in Table 2.

TABLE 2

n	1	2	3	4	5	6
$x_1^{(n)}$	0.9	0.82	1.03	1.01	1.00	1.00
$x_2^{(n)}$	1.6	2.22	2.07	2.00	1.99	2.00
$x_3^{(n)}$	4.0	3.15	3.03	2.97	3.00	3.00

We see that to within the required accuracy we have

$$x_1^{(5)} = x_1^{(6)}, \; x_2^{(5)} = x_2^{(6)}, \; x_3^{(5)} = x_3^{(6)}. \tag{71}$$

Setting $n = 5$ in (70) and taking account of (71), we see that to the required accuracy we have

$$x_1^{(5)} \approx 0.9 + 0.2x_2^{(5)} - 0.1x_3^{(5)},$$
$$x_2^{(5)} \approx 1.6 - 0.2x_1^{(5)} + 0.2x_3^{(5)},$$
$$x_3^{(5)} \approx 4 - 0.5x_1^{(5)} - 0.25x_2^{(5)}.$$

Actually these equations are exact (if we take 2 and not 1.99 for x_2), but this is not the point. It follows that, within the required degree of accuracy, the numbers $x_1^{(5)} = 1.00$, $x_2^{(5)} = 2.00$, $x_3^{(5)} = 3.00$, form a solution to our system.

We proceed in the same way in the general case. Suppose we are given the system (68). We take x_1 from the first equation, x_2 from the second, and so on. If, as we are assuming, none of the coefficients a_{ii} is zero, the system (68) assumes the form

$$x_1 = \frac{b_1}{a_{11}} - \qquad\qquad -\frac{a_{12}}{a_{11}}x_2 - \dots \qquad\qquad -\frac{a_{1m}}{a_{11}}x_m,$$

$$x_2 = \frac{b_2}{a_{22}} - \frac{a_{21}}{a_{22}}x_1 - \qquad\qquad \dots \qquad\qquad -\frac{a_{2m}}{a_{22}}x_m,$$

$$\cdot \quad \cdot \quad \cdot \quad \cdot \quad \cdot \quad \cdot \quad \cdot \quad \cdot \quad \cdot \quad \cdot \quad \cdot \quad \cdot$$

$$x_m = \frac{b_m}{a_{mm}} - \frac{a_{m1}}{a_{mm}}x_1 - \frac{a_{m2}}{a_{mm}}x_2 - \dots - \frac{a_{m,\,m-1}}{a_{mm}}x_{m-1}. \tag{72}$$

Suppose $x_1^{(1)}, \dots, x_m^{(1)}$ are any first approximations to the unknowns $x_1, \dots, x_m$. Substituting in the right side of (72), we find a system of second approximations to the required roots:

$$x_1^{(2)} = \frac{b_1}{a_{11}} - \qquad\qquad -\frac{a_{12}}{a_{11}}x_2^{(1)} - \dots \qquad\qquad -\frac{a_{1m}}{a_{11}}x_m^{(1)},$$

$$x_2^{(2)} = \frac{b_2}{a_{22}} - \frac{a_{21}}{a_{22}}x_1^{(1)} - \qquad\qquad \dots \qquad\qquad -\frac{a_{2m}}{a_{22}}x_m^{(1)},$$

$$\cdot \quad \cdot \quad \cdot \quad \cdot \quad \cdot \quad \cdot \quad \cdot \quad \cdot \quad \cdot \quad \cdot \quad \cdot \quad \cdot$$

$$x_2^{(2)} = \frac{b_m}{a_{mn}} - \frac{a_{m1}}{a_{mm}}x_1^{(1)} - \qquad\qquad \dots - \frac{a_{m,\,m-1}}{a_{mm}}x_{m-1}^{(1)}.$$

In the same way, having found a system of nth approximations

$x_1^{(n)}, \ldots, x_m^{(n)}$ to our unknowns, we find the next approximations by means of the formulas

$$x_1^{(n+1)} = \frac{b_1}{a_{11}} - \qquad\qquad - \frac{a_{12}}{a_{11}} x_2^{(n)} - \ldots \qquad\qquad - \frac{a_{1m}}{a_{11}} x_m^{(n)},$$

$$x_2^{(n+1)} = \frac{b_2}{a_{22}} - \frac{a_{21}}{a_{22}} x_1^{(n)} - \qquad\qquad \ldots \qquad\qquad - \frac{a_{2m}}{a_{22}} x_m^{(n)},$$

$$\cdots \cdots \cdots \cdots \cdots \cdots \cdots \cdots \cdots \cdots \cdots$$

$$x_m^{(n+1)} = \frac{b_m}{a_{mm}} - \frac{a_{m1}}{a_{mm}} x_1^{(n)} - \qquad\qquad \ldots - \frac{a_{m,\,m-1}}{a_{mm}} x_{m-1}^{(n)}. \qquad (73)$$

It can be shown that this sequence of successive approximations converges to the (unique) system of solutions if for every k we have the inequality

$$a_{kk} > |a_{k1}| + |a_{k2}| + \ldots + |a_{k,k-1}| + |a_{k,k+1}| + \ldots + |a_{km}|,$$

where $k = 1, \ldots, m$ or if

$$\sum_{j=1}^{m} \sum_{k=1}^{m} \left| \frac{a_{jk}}{a_{kk}} \right|^2 < m + 1.$$

Roughly speaking, the diagonal elements must be very large and positive. This restriction may appear to be very severe. However, there exist methods for reducing *any* system of linear equations (with as many unknowns as equations) to one in which these conditions hold (see, for example, Margulis: *Systems of Linear Equations*, Vol. 14 in this series).

The remarks made in Chapter 5 hold here, too. For instance, the result does not depend on our choice of an initial approximation. Thus a mistake in the course of our calculations does not make all our work useless, but merely lengthens it. Moreover, if the sequence converges, as it will if the indicated conditions are satisfied, it will always converge to a solution of the system (in general there is not a unique solution, but under our conditions there is).

The method we described may be modified in a number of ways. For example, having found an approximate value $x_1^{(n+1)}$, we find the approximation $x_2^{(n+1)}$ by substituting the values $x_1^{(n+1)}, x_3^{(n)}, \ldots, x_m^{(n)}$ for the unknowns in the right side of the second equation; then we find $x_3^{(n+1)}$ by substituting $x_1^{(n+1)}, x_2^{(n+1)}, x_4^{(n)}, \ldots, x_m^{(n)}$ in the third equation, and so on. A description of all the methods used for approximating a solution for a system of linear equations could easily fill a booklet of this size.

19

SUCCESSIVE APPROXIMATIONS IN GEOMETRY

We have now described applications of the method of successive approximation for solving equations and systems of equations. This method may also be applied to certain questions of geometry. We shall show how it may be used to obtain a value for the circumference of a circle. It is well known that we may approximate a circle successively by an inscribed square, regular octagon, 16-gon, . . . and find the circumference of the circle as the limit of the perimeters of these polygons. We calculate each perimeter with the help of the previous one.

Let us denote the side of our regular 2^n-gon by A_n, and its circumference by P_n. For example, A_2 is the side of an inscribed square, and therefore equals $R\sqrt{2}$, and $P_2 = 4R\sqrt{2}$. Suppose we have already found P_n. Then clearly

$$A_n = \frac{P_n}{2^n}.$$

Now the side A_{n+1} of an inscribed regular 2^{n+1}-gon may be expressed in terms of the side A_n of a regular 2^n-gon and the radius R by means of the formula

$$A_{n+1} = R\sqrt{\left[2 - \sqrt{\left(4 - \frac{A_n^2}{R^2}\right)}\right]}. \tag{74}$$

This may be proved geometrically, but it is faster by trigonometry. Thus we have

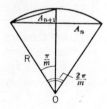

$$A_n = 2R\sin\frac{\pi}{m} \quad \text{and} \quad A_{n+1} = 2R\sin\frac{\pi}{2m}$$
$$(M = 2^n)$$

(see sketch). Now since for any α we have

$$\sin\frac{\alpha}{2} = \sqrt{\left(\frac{1 - \cos\alpha}{2}\right)},$$

we see that

$$A_{n+1} = 2R \sin \frac{\pi}{2m} = 2R \sqrt{\left(\frac{1 - \cos \frac{\pi}{n}}{2} \right)}$$

$$= R \sqrt{\left[2 - 2 \sqrt{\left(1 - \sin^2 \frac{\pi}{m} \right)} \right]} = R \sqrt{\left[2 - \sqrt{\left(4 - \frac{A_n}{R^2} \right)} \right]}.$$

This formula can now be used to calculate the perimeters. Recall that

$$A_n = \frac{P_n}{2^n} \quad \text{and} \quad A_{n+1} = \frac{P_{n+1}}{2^{n+1}};$$

consequently we have

$$P_{n+1} = 2^{n+1} R \sqrt{\left[2 - \sqrt{\left(4 - \frac{P_n^2}{2^n R^2} \right)} \right]}. \tag{75}$$

The sequence of numbers $P_2, P_3, \ldots, P_n, \ldots$ tends to the length of the circumference (to $2\pi R$). Thus the formula (75) may be regarded as a formula for the calculation of $2\pi R$ by the method of successive approximation. Using it, and taking $R = 1$, we may calculate the value of π to any number of decimal places.

There is another method of approximating π, known as the method of equal perimeters. We replace the regular 2^n-gon by a regular 2^{n+1}-gon with the same perimeter and the same center. We denote the length of the apothem of the regular 2^n-gon by l_n, and the radius of its circumcircle by r_n. (The apothem of a regular polygon is a line drawn from the center and perpendicular to a side.) We denote the length of the apothem and radius of the regular 2^{n+1}-gon with the same perimeter by l_{n+1} and r_{n+1}, respectively.

Let AB (Fig. 15) be a side of a 2^n-gon inscribed in a circle of radius r_n. We join the center C of the arc AB to A and B, and then draw DE parallel to AB and bisecting CF. It is clear that angle DOE is half angle AOB. So DE is a side of a regular 2^{n+1}-gon, inscribed in a circle of radius OD. Since $DE = \frac{1}{2}AB$, the perimeter of this 2^{n+1}-gon is the same as that of our 2^n-gon. This means that $r_{n+1} = OD$, $l_{n+1} = OK$.

We easily verify that

$$l_{n+1} = \frac{r_n + l_n}{2}. \tag{76}$$

By considering the right triangle ODC we also see that

$$r_{n+1} = \sqrt{(r_n l_{n+1})}. \tag{77}$$

Formulas (76) and (77) give r_{n+1} and l_{n+1} in terms of r_n and l_n.

As n increases, the perimeters of the polygons do not change, and the numbers r_n and l_n tend to the same limit. This limit is the

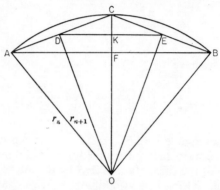

Fig. 15

radius of a circle whose circumference has the same length as the perimeters of all our polygons. If we choose our first polygon to have perimeter 2, then our limit circle will have perimeter 2, so that $2 = 2\pi R$, and $R = 1/\pi$. Thus

$$\lim_{n \to \infty} r_n = R = \frac{1}{\pi}; \quad \lim_{n \to \infty} l_n = R = \frac{1}{\pi}.$$

If we choose as our first polygon a square of side $\frac{1}{2}$, then $r_2 = \frac{1}{4}\sqrt{2}$, $l_2 = \frac{1}{4}$. We thus have the following assertion: if we put $r_2 = \frac{1}{4}\sqrt{2}$, $l_2 = \frac{1}{4}$ and calculate r_{n+1}, l_{n+1} ($n = 2, 3, \ldots$) by means of the formulas (76) and (77), then

$$\lim_{n \to \infty} r_n = \lim_{n \to \infty} l_n = \frac{1}{\pi}.$$

66

These formulas allow us to find an approximate value for $1/\pi$. To obtain $1/\pi$ to within a given error ε, all we need do is continue the process until we find an n for which r_n and l_n differ by less than 2ε. For we may easily show that $1/\pi$ lies between r_n and l_n (whatever the value of n), and therefore in this case within ε of l_{n+1}.

20

CONCLUSION

In this book we have seen how the method of successive approximation can be applied to a variety of problems: the drawing of plans, extraction of roots, solution of equations, calculation of the circumference of a circle. The wealth of applications of the method is by no means exhausted by these examples. Many problems lead to differential equations (in which we are required to find a function which satisfies equations in which its derivatives enter), to integral equations, and to even more complex equations. One of the most powerful methods of approximate solution of such equations is, once again, the method of successive approximation (iteration). Of course, its application in such cases is more involved than in the solution of algebraic equations (the only sort we have considered). But we may safely say that without the use of methods of successive approximation we would not be able to tackle any of the impressive problems in physics and engineering (such as sending a rocket around the moon) that are constantly being solved nowadays. Not only the calculation of satellite orbits, but the calculations needed to start an atomic reactor, to study the structure of the atom, or to forecast the weather, all use this method. But a discussion of the applications of the method beyond the field of elementary mathematics would take us outside the scope of this book.

EXERCISES

Here are some exercises which the reader may use to check his mastery of the material of this book.

Use the method of iteration (p. 48) to solve these equations:†

1. $x = \dfrac{1}{(x+1)^2}$.　　**2.** $x = (x+1)^3$.　　**3.** $x = 4 + \sqrt[3]{\dfrac{x-1}{x+1}}$.

4. $x = 2 \pm \sqrt[4]{x}$.　　**5.** $x = \sqrt[3]{(5-x)}$.　　**6.** $4 - 3x = \tan x$.

7. $x^2 = \sin x$.　　**8.** $x^3 = \sin x$.　　**9.** $x = \arcsin\dfrac{x+1}{4}$.　　**10.** $x = \cos x$.

11. $x = \text{arc-cos}\,\dfrac{1}{x}$.　　**12.** $x = 1 + \dfrac{1}{10}\sin x$.　　**13.** $x = \pm \sqrt{[(\log(x+2)]}$.

14. $x^2 = \ln(x+1)$.　　**15.** $\ln x = 4 - x^2$.　　**16.** $\ln x = 2 - x$.

17. $x^2 = e^x + 2$.　　**18.** $\log x = 0.1\,x$.　　**19.** $x = \arctan(\log x)$.

20. $x = \dfrac{1}{10}e^{-x}$.

Use the method of chords and tangents (p. 43) to solve these equations:

21. $x^3 - 5x + 1 = 0$.　　　　**22.** $x^3 - 9x^2 + 20x - 1 = 0$.

23. $x^3 - 3x^2 - 3x + 10 = 0$.　　**24.** $x^5 + 5x + 1 = 0$.

25. $\sin x + x = 1$.　　　　　**26.** $x^2 - 10\log x - 3 = 0$.

† In some of these examples the reader must first rewrite the equations in the form $x = \varphi(x)$.

ANSWERS

1. $x = 0.4655$. **2.** $x = -2.325$. **3.** $x_1 = 4.870$; $x_2 = -0.9840$.
4. $x_1 = 1.000$; $x_2 = 3.343$. **5.** $x = 1.516$. **6.** One of the solutions is
$x = 0.9082$. **7.** $x_1 = 0.0000$; $x_2 = 0.8768$. **8.** $x_1 = 0.0000$; $x_{2,3}$
$= 0.9286$. **9.** $x_1 = 2.209$; $x_2 = 0.3422$; $x_3 = -2.702$. **10.** $x = 0.7478$.
11. One of the solutions is $x = 4.914$. **12.** $x = 1.088$. **13.** $x_1 = 0.6507$;
$x_2 = -0.4397$. **14.** $x_1 = 0$; $x_2 = 0.7469$. **15.** $x = 2.841$. **16.** x
$= 1.557$. **17.** $x = -1.492$. **18.** $x_1 = 10$; $x_2 = 1.371$. **19.** One of the
solutions is $x = 3.654$. **20.** $x = 0.0913$. **21.** $x_1 = -2.33$; $x_2 = 0.20$;
$x_3 = 2.12$. **22.** $x_1 = 0.843$; $x_2 = 2.217$; $x_3 = 5.949$. **23.** $x_1 =$
-1.7912; $x_2 = 2.0000$; $x_3 = 2.7912$. **24.** $x = 0.1999$. **25.** $x = 0.5110$.
26. $x_1 = 0.535$; $x_2 = 0.270$.

ERRATA

Page 2:
Equation (2)
$$x = p + \sqrt{(p^2 - q)}. \tag{2}$$
should read: $x = p \pm \sqrt{(p^2 - q)}$. (2)

Page 12:
10 lines from foot of page:
solve this equation exactly, we obtain the roots $\alpha_1 = -5 \pm \sqrt{28}$.
should read:
solve this equation exactly, we obtain the root $\alpha_1 = -5 + \sqrt{28}$.

Page 14:
21 lines from top of page:
  To do so we compare the errors $\alpha_n = \sqrt{a} - x_n$ and α_{n+1}
should read:
  To do so we compare the errors $\alpha_n = \sqrt{a} - x_n$ and $\alpha_{n+1} =$

Page 24:
5 lines from foot of page:
$$f'(x) = ka_0 x^{k-1} + (k-1)a_1 x^{k-2} + \ldots + a^k_{-1}. \tag{33}$$
should read:
$$f'(x) = ka_0 x^{k-1} + (k-1)a_1 x^{k-2} + \ldots + a_k^{-1}. \tag{33}$$

Page 54:
3 lines from top of page:
$$\leqslant \frac{|\sin x| + |\cos x|}{4} \leqslant \frac{1}{2} \text{ for all } x,$$
should read:
$$\leqslant \frac{|\sin x| + |\cos x|}{4} < \frac{1}{2} \text{ for all } x,$$